Sheep and Goat Practice

The *In Practice* Handbooks Series

Series Editor: Edward Boden

Past and present members of *In Practice* Editorial Board

Titles in print:
Feline Practice
Canine Practice
Equine Practice
Bovine Practice
Sheep and Goat Practice
Swine Practice

The *In Practice* Handbooks

Sheep and Goat Practice

Edited by E. Boden
Executive Editor, *In Practice*

Baillière Tindall

LONDON   PHILADELPHIA   TORONTO   SYDNEY   TOKYO

Baillière Tindall   24–28 Oval Road
W. B. Saunders   London NW1 7DX

The Curtis Center
Independence Square West
Philadelphia, PA 19106–3399, USA

55 Horner Avenue
Toronto, Ontario, M8Z 4X6, Canada

Harcourt Brace Jovanovich Group
(Australia) Pty Ltd
30–52 Smidmore Street
Marrickville
NSW 2204, Australia

Harcourt Brace Jovanovich Japan Inc
Ichibancho Central Building
22–1 Ichibancho
Chiyoda-ku, Tokyo 102, Japan

© 1991 Baillière Tindall

Typeset by Photo·graphics, Honiton, Devon
Printed and bound in Hong Kong by Dah Hua Printing Press Co., Ltd.

A catalogue record for this book is available from
the British Library

ISBN 0–7020–1555–5

Contents

DISEASE

Contributors

G. Aitchison Department of Pathology, Animal Diseases Research Association, Moredun Research Institute, 408 Gilmerton Road, Edinburgh EH17 7JH, UK

I. D. Aitken Director, Animal Diseases Research Association, Moredun Research Institute, 408 Gilmerton Road, Edinburgh EH17 7JH, UK

W. T. Appleyard Senior Veterinary Investigation Officer, Scottish Veterinary Investigation Service, Cleeve Gardens, Oakbank Road, Perth, Perthshire PH1 1HF, UK

H. D. Bailie Coopers Animal Health Ltd, Berkhamstead Hill, Berkhamstead, Herts HP4 2QE, UK

I. Baker Tuckett Gray & Partners, 49 Cambridge Street, Aylesbury, Bucks HP20 1RP, UK

R. Barlow Professor of Veterinary Pathology, University of London, Royal Veterinary College, Hawkshead Campus, Hawkshead Lane, North Mymms, Hatfield, Herts AL9 7TA, UK

H. Buttle AFRC Institute of Grassland and Environmental Research, Hurley, Maidenhead, Berks SL6 5LR, UK

M. Dawson Department of Virology, Central Veterinary Laboratory, New Haw, Weybridge, Surrey KT15 3NB, UK

A. Eales The Swifts, 1 New Winton, New Winton, Tranent, East Lothian EH33 2NH, UK

J. Gilmour Moredun Research Institute, 408 Gilmerton Road, Edinburgh EH17 7JH, UK

N. J. L. Gilmour Principal Veterinary Research Officer, Moredun Research Institute, 408 Gilmerton Road, Edinburgh EH17 7JH, UK

D. C. Henderson Department of Clinical Studies, Animal Diseases Research Association, Moredun Research Institute, 408 Gilmerton Road, Edinburgh EH17 7JH, UK

P. G. G. Jackson University Physician, Medical Division, Department of Clinical Veterinary Medicine, University of Cambridge, Madingley Road, Cambridge CB3 0ES, UK

K. Linklater Director Scottish Agricultural Colleges Veterinary Investigation Service, Oakbank Road, Perth PH1 1HG, UK

J. C. Low Veterinary Investigation Officer, The Scottish Agricultural Colleges Veterinary Investigation Service, Veterinary Investigation Centre, Bush Estate, Penicuik, Midlothian EH26 0QE, UK

A. Mews Assistant Chief Veterinary Officer and Head of Farm Animals Department, RSPCA, Causeway, Horsham, West Sussex RH12 1HG, UK

G. B. B. Mitchell Veterinary Investigation Officer, Scottish Agricultural Colleges, Veterinary Investigation Service, Auchincruive, Ayr KA6 5AE, UK

K. L. Morgan Department of Veterinary Medicine, University of Bristol, Langford House, Langford, Bristol BS18 7DU, UK

A. Mowlem The Goat Advisory Bureau, 9 Pitts Lane, Earley, Reading RG6 1BX, UK

P. Nettleton Moredun Research Institute, 408 Gilmerton Road, Edinburgh, Midlothian EH17 7JH, UK

H. W. Reid Department of Microbiology, Animal Diseases Research Association, Moredun Research Institute, 408 Gilmerton Road, Edinburgh EH17 7JH, UK

A. J. F. Russel Macaulay Lane Use Research Institute, Pentlandfield, Roslin, Midlothian EH26 0PY, UK

J. A. Spence Department of Pathology, Animal Diseases Research Association, Moredun Research Institute, 408 Gilmerton Road, Edinburgh EH17 7JH, UK

I. R. White Macaulay Land Use Research Institute, Pentland-field, Roslin, Midlothian EH26 0PY, UK

Foreword

In Practice was started in 1979 as a clinical supplement to *The Veterinary Record*. Its carefully chosen, highly illustrated articles specially commissioned from leaders in their field were aimed specifically at the practitioner. They have proved extremely popular with experienced veterinarians and students alike. The editorial board, chaired for the first 10 years by Professor James Armour, was particularly concerned to emphasize differential diagnosis.

In response to consistent demand, articles from *In Practice*, updated and revised by the authors, are now published in convenient handbook form. Each book deals with a particular species or group of related animals.

E. Boden

Production and Control

CHAPTER 1

Body Condition Scoring of Sheep

ANGUS RUSSEL

INTRODUCTION

Body condition scoring of sheep is now widely used by the agricultural advisory services and livestock producers as an aid to flock management. The technique is simply a means of subjectively assessing the degree of fatness or condition of the live animal and as such is not new.

Stockmen have always appraised the condition of their animals, describing them in terms such as "lean", "forward store", "fair to middling", "not too bad", "fit" or "rolling fat". One of the difficulties of such descriptions is that they are all relative so that a ewe which, for example, might be considered by a low-ground flockmaster to be in only moderate condition could be judged as "very good" by someone accustomed to handling hill stock.

Over the years a number of attempts have been made to formalize condition scoring using numerical values in place of the often more colourful but frequently ambiguous verbal descriptions. Many of these systems used a 10 point scale but have failed to stand the test of time, probably because of the difficulty of defining clear differences between one point and the next.

A system based on a six point scale and developed in

collaboration with Dr R. L. Reid, was described by Jeffries (1961) and advocated as an aid to sheep management under Australian pastoral conditions. Using this system as a basis, Russel *et al.* (1969) showed that subjectively assessed condition score was closely related to the amount of chemically determined fat in sheep and that it could provide an acceptable and useful means of estimating the proportion of fat in the animal body.

This system, for sheep, has now been adopted by the Meat and Livestock Commission and advisory services throughout the United Kingdom and has also proved to be a useful tool in certain areas of research, particularly in studies on sheep production. Its success relies principally on the clear definition of each of the six grades or scores in terms of readily identifiable anatomical characteristics (see below) which enables the technique to be learned easily and which helps to ensure a high degree of consistency between scorers.

CONDITION SCORING

Condition score is assessed by palpation of the ewe in the lumbar region, on and around the backbone in the loin area immediately behind the last rib and above the kidneys (Fig. 1.1).

(1) An assessment is made of the prominence (the degree of sharpness or roundness) of the spinous processes of the lumbar vertebrae.

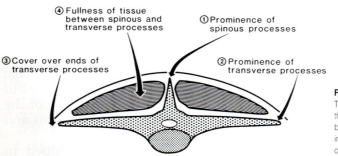

④ Fullness of tissue between spinous and transverse processes

① Prominence of spinous processes

③ Cover over ends of transverse processes

② Prominence of transverse processes

Fig. 1.1
The four stages in the assessment of body condition score in the lumbar region of sheep.

(2)   The prominence of, and the degree of fat cover over, the transverse processes of the vertebrae are assessed.

(3)   The extent of the muscular and fatty tissues below the transverse processes is judged by the ease with which the fingers pass under the ends of these bones.

(4)   The fullness of the eye muscle area and its degree of fat cover in the angle between the spinous and transverse processes is estimated.

Animals are then awarded a score on the following scale:

Score 0 – Extremely emaciated and on the point of death. It is not possible to detect any muscular or fatty tissue between the skin and the bone.

Score 1 – The spinous processes are felt to be prominent and sharp. The transverse processes are also sharp, the fingers pass easily under the ends and it is possible to feel between each process. The eye muscle areas are shallow with no fat cover.

Score 2 – The spinous processes still feel prominent, but smooth, and individual processes can be felt only as fine corrugations. The transverse processes are smooth and rounded, and it is possible to pass the fingers under the ends with a little pressure. The eye muscle areas are of moderate depth, but have little fat cover.

Score 3 – The spinous processes are detected only as small elevations; they are smooth and rounded, and individual bones can be felt only with pressure. The transverse processes are smooth and well covered, and firm pressure is required to feel over the ends. The eye muscle areas are full, and have a moderate degree of fat cover.

Score 4 – The spinous processes can just be detected, with pressure, as a hard line between the fat-covered muscle areas. The ends of the transverse processes cannot be felt. The eye muscle areas are full, and have a thick covering of fat.

Score 5 – The spinous processes cannot be detected even with firm pressure, and there is a depression between the layers of fat in the position where the spinous processes would normally be felt. The transverse processes cannot be detected. The eye muscle areas are very full with very thick fat cover. There may be large deposits of fat over the rump and tail.

In any flock it is unlikely that condition will range over more than two scores at any one time, or more than three scores over the whole year.

In practice, therefore, the range of fatness is narrower than that encompassed by the scoring system, and the scores 0–5, as set out above, became inadequate to describe variations within a flock. In this situation it becomes almost automatic to assess condition to the nearest half score.

There will always be some assessments falling midway between two points on the scale, even when half scores are used, but for all practical purposes half scores are sufficient.

USING THE SCORES

One of the advantages of using condition scoring as a tool in flock management is that it overcomes differences in body size and weight which exist between individuals within a flock and between flocks of different breeds.

The condition or fatness of a ewe has a major effect on its productivity. With individual animals liveweight is a good index of fatness, but differences in frame size between individual ewes within a breed and between different breeds make it difficult to formulate general recommendations as to appropriate liveweights at different stages of the annual cycle. Some generalizations can, however, be made on the basis of condition score.

BODY CONDITION AND REPRODUCTION

The times when condition scoring is particularly useful as an aid to flock management are before mating and during the period of pre-lambing feeding.

There is now a considerable amount of evidence relating body condition at mating to ovulation rate and lambing percentage (e.g. Doney *et al.*, 1982). In general, the better the body condition at mating, the higher the ovulation rate and thus the higher the potential lambing percentage.

Research results indicate that ewes should generally be in

condition score 3.5 at mating, although condition score 3 may be a more realistic target for hill ewes.

There is also evidence that overfatness at mating is associated with an increased level of barrenness. If the condition score of an appreciable proportion of the flock is greater than 3.5 at mating it is likely either that the production from these animals has been very poor earlier in the season or that stocking rates have been too low. In either case the system of management requires to be critically examined.

For a satisfactory lambing performance it is not sufficient to achieve an average condition score of 3.5 at mating for the flock as a whole, the aim should be to have *all* ewes in this condition at the time the rams are put out.

To achieve this all ewes must be condition scored 6–8 weeks before the beginning of mating, and the leaner ewes taken out for preferential treatment, i.e. given the best pasture and/or stocked more lightly.

At the same time any overfat ewes should be put on a nutritional regime which will ensure a reduction in weight and condition.

In some situations supplementary feeding of the leaner ewes may be justified. The poor condition of many of the leaner ewes two months before mating may be the result of the rearing of a good pair of twin lambs, and such ewes should be given every opportunity to produce twins again in the following season by giving them better feeding to improve body condition by mating time.

Examples given by the Meat and Livestock Commission (1983) of the response in lambing percentage to variation in body condition at mating include the results shown in Table 1.1.

PREGNANCY

Condition scoring before mating is thus essential for the achievement of high lambing percentages. It is also important in ensuring that the ewe has adequate body reserves on which to draw during the undernourishment which almost inevitably occurs in most flocks at some stage of pregnancy.

In some respects the ewe appears to regulate its ovulation

Table 1.1 Effect of body condition at mating on lambing percentage

	Body condition score at mating						
	1	1.5	2	2.5	3	3.5	4
Hill ewes							
Scottish blackface	–	79	–	–	162	–	–
Hill gritstone	–	–	75	103	119	109	–
Welsh mountain	60	65	105	116	123	–	–
Swaledale	–	78	133	140	156	–	–
Lowland							
Gritstone (lowland)	–	–	–	132	154	173	–
Masham	–	–	–	167	181	215	–
Mule	–	–	149	166	178	194	192
Greyface	–	–	147	163	176	189	184
Welsh halfbred	–	126	139	150	164	172	–
Scottish halfbred	–	–	148	170	183	217	202

rate and conception rate to the level of body fat reserves or condition at mating so that those with the highest foetal requirements have the greatest energy reserves on which to draw.

It should be noted, however, that in highly prolific breeds such as the Finn and Finn crosses, ovulation rate is less dependent on body condition at mating. The high foetal burdens in these breeds can place very considerable demands on body reserves in late pregnancy, and thus it is important to ensure that such ewes are in good condition at the beginning of pregnancy.

Ideally, loss of condition should be avoided during mating and for the first month of pregnancy by which stage implantation is complete. In some situations a small loss of condition may be inevitable at this time, but should be restricted to not more than one quarter of a condition score.

During the second and third months of pregnancy ewes which were in condition score 3.5 at mating can afford to lose some condition, and indeed there is evidence that this may be desirable. Such losses should not, however, exceed 0.75 of a score.

In late pregnancy ewes should be managed and fed according to body condition. Even in flocks where all ewes were in good condition at mating a proportion of the ewes will have become too lean by the beginning of late pregnancy.

All ewes should be condition scored about eight weeks before the beginning of lambing and those with a condition score of less than 2.5 separated from the main flock and given an extra 100–200 g supplementary feeding per day.

Ewes in condition score 2.5–3 eight weeks before lambing can afford to lose a further half of a condition score without prejudicing their lambing performance, but every effort must be made to prevent the condition of the poorer ewes falling below condition score 2 at lambing. Lambing does not signify the end of the period of dependence on body fat and some reserves must be husbanded for use in the early weeks of lactation.

THE TECHNIQUE IN PRACTICE

Body condition scoring is now an integral component of good flock management. It has the advantages of being readily learned and used and of not requiring any equipment. It is also particularly useful in situations where liveweight is difficult to interpret, e.g. during late pregnancy when the weight of foetuses and fluids contribute substantially to ewe liveweight.

There is a need, however, to check standards from time to time. For those who practise the technique infrequently or have little opportunity to compare standards with other users of the system there is no shame in referring to the above description of the different scores while refreshing one's memory, and having a trial run on a few sheep.

As a check on scoring standards, a difference of one unit of condition score is generally equivalent to about 13 % of the liveweight of non-pregnant ewes in moderate body condition.

Differences in conformation between breeds result in different relationships between condition score and the proportion of fat in the body. This is perhaps most evident in the Finn and Finn cross ewes which appear to have more prominent spinous processes than other breeds and which carry a greater proportion of their body fat around the internal organs. Such breed variations in conformation are relatively small and unimportant and do not require any exceptions to be made to the general recommendations on the use of condition scoring in flock management.

It must be remembered that the system is subjective and therefore has limitations. It attempts to put a continuous variable into discrete categories and there is thus a temptation to subdivide scores into ever smaller fractions. However small the divisions used there will always be some individual animals which fall midway between one and the next, and for most practical purposes there is little to be gained by attempting to score any more precisely than to the nearest half score.

REFERENCES

Doney, J. M., Gunn, R. G. & Horak, F. (1982). *Sheep and Goat Production* (ed. I. E. Coop). Elsevier, Amsterdam.

Jeffries, B. C. (1961). *Tasmanian Journal of Agriculture* **32**, 19.

Meat and Livestock Commission (1983). *Feeding the Ewe*, 2nd edn. MLC, Bletchley.

Russel, A. J. F., Doney, J. M. & Gunn, R. G. (1969). *Journal of Agricultural Science, Cambridge* **72**, 451.

CHAPTER 2

Control of the Breeding Season in Sheep and Goats

DAVID C. HENDERSON

INTRODUCTION

The most commonly used methods for the control and manipulation of the breeding season have been available for many years – the sponge (progestogen-impregnated pessary) for over a quarter of a century and the teaser ram for a good deal longer. Nevertheless, neither of these techniques is widely used in the UK, despite the undoubted value of each.

In recent years, however, these techniques have become more refined and better understood, due mainly to a handful of dedicated workers who have persevered – especially with the sponge – and are achieving consistently good results. This improvement has come from a better understanding of the essential supportive husbandry which must accompany these breeding programmes if optimum results are to be obtained.

THE RAM OR TEASER EFFECT

The use of teasers, although less versatile and less precise than the sponge, is a useful and underutilized method for shortening the lambing period and for encouraging ewes to start mating a week or two earlier than they would normally do. The sequence of events in a flock using teasers is illustrated in Fig. 2.1.

Ewes which have been deprived of the sight, sound and particularly the smell of rams for at least 4–6 weeks during the transitional period (late anoestrus–early breeding season) will respond to the presence of the male by ovulating within three or four days, but without any signs of behavioural oestrus, i.e. a "silent" oestrus. In a proportion of such ewes (40–60 %) a true oestrus with ovulation plus behavioural oestrus (and therefore a fertile one), will occur after about 18 days following the introduction of teasers (A in Fig. 2.1).

In the rest of the flock, the corpus luteum formed following the first "silent" oestrus regresses prematurely, followed by a second "silent" oestrus with ovulation and a corpus luteum which has a normal lifespan. These ewes therefore come into fertile oestrus from around day 23 following the introduction of teasers on day 0 (B in Fig. 2.1).

If fertile rams replace the teasers at around day 14, the majority of ewes in the flock will be served over an 8–10 day period from around day 18 onwards. Lambing can be reduced to four or five weeks with the bulk of lambing occurring over a 2–3 week period.

The best teasers are rams of high libido and they should have had some previous mating experience if possible. Shearlings or younger mature rams which are to be culled for some reason

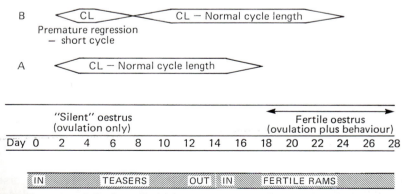

Fig. 2.1 Ram or "teaser" effect in transitional (late anoestrus – early breeding) season in sheep. Note that ewes must be separated from rams for at least a month before teasing.

such as poor conformation or poor lambing results, but which are still keen to work, are ideal.

The vasectomy operation is straightforward. A length of vas deferens should be removed and squeezed on to a glass slide to check for the presence of sperm. The cut ends should be doubled back and sutured to the tunica to prevent recanalization, slight though the risk may be. Teasers should be prepared well in advance of the period of use and should be tested for sterility by electroejaculation immediately before joining the ewes.

The teaser effect is due to pheromones from the wool and wool wax of rams, and workers in New Zealand are endeavouring to produce a synthetic ram pheromone.

Androgenized wethers can also be used as teasers, with roughly equal success. Wethers should be injected weekly, for three weeks, with 100–150 mg of testosterone (proprionate or cyclopentyl proprionate). The effect persists for some 4–5 weeks after the third treatment.

It is worth remembering that although the spread of a synchronized oestrus in teased flocks is wider than in sponged flocks, a higher than normal ram to ewe ratio, say 5 %, should be used to achieve optimum results. Teasing will encourage a group of ewes to start oestrous cycling in the transitional period, but the method is somewhat variable and is not suitable for true out-of-season breeding as it is practised at present.

BUCK EFFECT

While the buck effect has not been as well defined as the ram effect it is clearly very similar and could be put to practical use. Also the detrimental effect of ignoring the phenomenon should not be forgotten. In order to obtain a well synchronized response and to advance the breeding season, does must be in late anoestrus or transition. Once does have started oestrous cycling the presence of the buck will not alter the timing of oestrous events. Does must have been isolated from bucks for at least 3–4 weeks prior to teasing.

Teaser bucks need only be introduced to does for a short time to produce this effect, since the hormonal response from does (luteinizing hormone pulse frequency) is almost instantaneous. Entire bucks should replace teasers two and a half weeks after the introduction of teasers so that a fertile mating can take place at the double peak of oestrus that follows – a regime similar to that used in sheep only with the timings adjusted to take account of the different oestrous cycle length and type of response in does.

USE OF SPONGES IN SHEEP

Sponges (progestogen-impregnated pessaries) used on their own within the breeding season are undoubtedly the most reliable and versatile method of manipulating the breeding season in sheep. Providing the basic rules are adhered to they will give consistently good results. If disappointing results are obtained then it is likely to be husbandry and management which are at fault and not the sponges.

When used outside the breeding season it is necessary to use a follicle stimulating hormone, usually pregnant mares' serum gonadotrophin (PMSG), at the end of the progestogen priming period (with sponges) in order to initiate a fertile oestrus following sponge removal. At this time two difficult decisions have to be made. First, is PMSG necessary and secondly, if so, at what dosage?

Progestogen sponges alone will produce a response only from ewes which are already sexually active and undergoing normal oestrous cycles at regular 16 or 17 day intervals. To achieve a well synchronized oestrus in a flock *all* ewes must be cycling and this means that the shepherd must be familiar with the breeding season for that particular flock.

TIMING OF INSERTION

As a guide, particularly where past records of lambing for the flock are available, the day by which 50 % of the previously unsynchronized flock have lambed should be calculated and sponges inserted not earlier than 150 days before this day, if PMSG is not to be used. While there are differences from year to year, records over a few years will provide a useful guide.

Alternatively, raddled teaser rams can be used three or four weeks before intended sponge insertion, to ascertain the proportion of ewes which are cycling and also to encourage those not already cycling to do so.

PMSG DOSAGE

The second question, that of PMSG dosage, is more difficult. There are so many breeds and cross-breeds of sheep in the UK and such a diversity of management systems and seasons of lambing, that there are no statistically significant data on which to base advice.

The general rule is that the dose of PMSG should be sufficient to initiate a fertile oestrus after progestogen priming, but insufficient to cause superovulation and therefore the birth of large litters of low birth weight lambs with a reduced chance of survival.

Table 2.1 is a guide for PMSG use and dosage, but it must be emphasized that it is only a guide, based on the experience of the author and others, often under widely differing conditions. PMSG is supplied as a freeze-dried preparation which should be made up immediately before use. Veterinary surgeons should ensure that their clients are aware of this, since the potency of the reconstituted product deteriorates rapidly.

Table 2.1 Guide to PMSG dosage in synchronized (sponged) flocks.

| | Sheep | | | |
Month	Dorset horn Finn/Dorsets	Suffolk Suffolk cross	Scottish half-breds, mules, greyfaces	Goats
July	600–500*	750–600	Poor results	600–500
August	400–300	500–400	750–600	500–400
September	0	300–0	500–300	300–0
October	0	0	0	0

*Dosages in international units.

OUT-OF-SEASON BREEDING WITH SPONGES

When breeding out of season it is unwise to be too ambitious and attempt to do so too far into anoestrus, since results may be disappointing or economically unacceptable. It should be remembered that the effect of day length in anoestrus will mean the ewes which do not conceive to first service will fail to return to a "repeat" oestrus. This should not be a problem in the transitional period, however.

A timetable for planning synchronized breeding programme in flocks is suggested in Table 2.2. Programmes should be tailor-made to suit individual flock circumstances.

The lambing pattern in a flock of greyface ewes is shown in Fig. 2.4 and the compactness of lambing in a sponged flock compared with flocks using teasers and natural service is illustrated in Fig. 2.5. Table 2.4 presents results from a flock in which a large group of ewes was required to lamb over one week during March and shows the excellent results which can be obtained by attention to detail.

USE OF SPONGES IN GOATS

Most breeds of goats kept in the UK have a fairly restricted breeding season – from around September to February. This poses problems for milk producers in maintaining a regular supply of fresh (as opposed to frozen) milk to their customers.

Progestogen sponges can help in the goat herd in a number of ways and, in general, work very well for

(1)   Batching kiddings to even out milk supplies.
(2)   Early and late season breeding to extend the milking period.
(3)   Out-of-season breeding to attempt to maintain year-round milk supplies. The lactation curve is flatter in goats than in dairy cows and even though milking can continue for up to 24 months at reasonable yield, some herd owners prefer to maintain a 365-day kidding index, not least because of the extra crop of kids for replacement and for sale (especially where markets for goat meat are established).
(4)   Herds using artificial insemination.

(5) Small herds with no males, where females have to be transported to the male for service.

The oestrous cycle of the goat (18–22 days) is some two or three days longer than that of the ewe and this has led some to the practice of leaving sponges in does for periods of up to 17–21 days in some instances. In the author's experience this is not necessary because a 14-day insertion (as in ewes) gives equivalent results.

Goats protest more than sheep at sponge insertion (and indeed at most other procedures!) and gentle handling is essential. In maiden and smaller animals sponges can be difficult to insert using the applicators provided and sponges should be lubricated (minimally) and inserted using a clean finger.

Sponged goats show a very strong oestrus – most being in heat by 36–48 hours after sponge removal. When breeding out of season the main problem is that while male goats will usually mate, the quantity and quality of their semen is relatively poor. As in rams, a suitable daylight regime can help in this regard, but this may not always be practical and an adequate number of males must be provided. Handmating techniques and artificial insemination can help overcome this problem.

PMSG DOSAGE IN GOATS

There is very little information available from goat herds and what there is is not very objective. As with ewes, season, breed, prolificacy, lactational status and other relevant factors should be taken into account. The dosages in Table 2.1 are given as a rough guide only.

PROSTAGLANDINS FOR SYNCHRONIZATION OF OESTRUS

Prostaglandin F_2 alpha (PGF_2-α) and its analogues cause regression of the corpus luteum and can therefore be used to synchronize oestrus, but only during the breeding season. They therefore have no place in early or out-of-season breeding,

Table 2.2 Sheep breeding management timetable for sponged flocks.

Day	Operation
−120	*Plan breeding programme in detail* Done by the farmer in consultation with his or her veterinary surgeon and specialist sheep adviser. Practical and economic feasibilities should be rigorously examined.
	Identify suitable ewes and rams The correct breed of ewe for out-of-season breeding or for frequent breeding flocks is crucial (e.g. Finn × Dorsets). A high ram to ewe ratio is essential (10 % minimum) at the induced oestrus. Do not attempt a synchronized oestrus if sufficient rams are not available, unless artificial insemination is to be used.
−90	*Wean lambs/condition score ewes* Ewes should be grouped according to condition score and fed appropriately. Ewes in very fat condition will need to lose weight at this time. Keep ewes well away from rams until day 0.
−60	*Ram health and fertility check – flushing rams* If, after a thorough examination, there is some doubt about the fertility of a ram a semen sample should be examined. There is no place for doubtful rams in a synchronized programme. Rams should reach condition score 4 by mating and require a longer flushing period than ewes. A high protein ration has been advocated to improve sperm production. Any ewes from traditional March–April lambing flocks which are to be transferred to an early breeding flock must be weaned by now otherwise lactational anoestrus will interfere with the results.
−30	*Condition score ewes and "flush"* Check that target condition score can be achieved and adjust feeding accordingly, remembering that it takes three weeks to put on half a condition score.
−14	*Insert sponges* Sponges can be inserted by shepherds but they will need instruction from a veterinary surgeon before their first attempt (Figs 2.2 and 2.3). Stress gentleness and hygiene. Sponges should be left *in situ* for 12–14 days.

−2   *Remove sponges – inject PMSG if necessary*

On removal there will be an accumulation of vaginal mucus with a characteristic smell. This should clear up quickly and should not interfere with conception. (Shepherds should be aware of the possibility of fly-strike around the vulva in hot weather with undipped sheep.) Where PMSG is required it should be given at the time of sponge removal. Earlier administration (e.g. two days before sponge removal) makes little difference to the result, but means another unnecessary gathering.

0   *Rams joined with ewes*

It is crucial to use an adequate number of suitably fit and fertile rams – at least 10 %. It is most important also that rams are not joined with the ewes until 48 hours after sponge removal so as to avoid rams depleting their semen reserves on the first few ewes that come into oestrus (see Table 2.3). There is no need to raddle rams at the first induced oestrus as most of the ewes will be served. Indeed, as rams are very busy the harnesses may rub them sore if they are not fitted snugly and this may dull their desire to mount.

2   *Rams withdrawn*

After two days of mating it is best to pull the rams out and to feed them some concentrate to attempt to maintain body condition, which tends to "melt" from rams during the tupping period.

16   *Rejoin rams*

Raddles must be employed at this time to identify ewes which will lamb in the second half of lambing. Use at least 3 % rams and leave them in for one week.

24   *Rams withdrawn – teasers joined*

Allowing only two services produces a compact lambing and can improve flock fertility over the years by selecting against ewes which are reluctant to breed early. Raddled teasers (1 %) will identify barren ewes which can be fattened up and checked by scanning for pregnancy before sale.

Avoid stressing ewes during the early weeks of pregnancy by postponing all routine tasks (especially dipping) if possible. This will keep early embryonic loss to a minimum which will, in turn, increase lambing rate and reduce barren rate.

continued

Table 2.2 Continued.

Day	Operation
60–100	*Pregnancy diagnosis by ultrasound scanning* "Real-time" scanning will identify barren ewes and single- and multiple-bearing ewes. Time the scanning to cover both first and repeat service groups as near to 60–70 days as possible. Resist the urge to do this task earlier (see "stress" above). Feed ewes according to foetal number (White and Russel, 1984).
	Housing of ewes Synchronized flocks must be housed over the lambing period. This should be planned now if ewes are not housed over the entire winter period. Organize all labour, housing (including individual lambing pens) and equipment (warming box, stomach tubes, etc.) and obtain medicines well in advance.
142–150	*Lambing – 1st service group* Close shepherding – for 24 hours a day by shift working – will pay handsomely in terms of lambs saved over this short period of 5–7 days. From 65–85 % of ewes should lamb in this group.
151–157	*No lambings for one week* Clean out lambing area and bed liberally with straw (especially lambing pens) or prepare fresh area for later lambings.
158–170	*Lambing – "repeat" group* Close shepherding once again – many lambs are lost through neglect towards the end of lambing.
	Record lambing results Use data to help plan next season's programme. Health control measures should be built on to such a programme.

Fig. 2.2 Insertion and (far right) removal of progestogen-impregnated sponge.

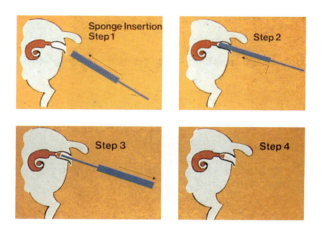

Fig. 2.3
Diagrammatic
representation of
sponge insertion.

Table 2.3 Effect of timing of ram introduction on conception rate after sponge/PMSG treatment in late anoestrus.

	Rams in at sponge removal	Rams in 48 hours after sponge removal
Number of ewes†	79	80
Number mated at induced oestrus	76 (96 %)	77 (96 %)
Conceptions at induced oestrus	30 (40 %)	52 (68 %)*
Number of lambs born	43 (1.43)	80 (1.54)

*Difference significant at $P < 0.01$.
†16 groups of 10 ewes; 1 ram per 10 ewes.
Data from Boland and Gordon (1979).

except where they are used along with progestogen sponges and pregnant mares' serum gonadotrophin.

Both single and double treatment regimes are used in the ewe and the doe and are similar to those used in the cow. There is debate as to the most appropriate timing between double injections. The literature records intervals of 9–15 days in the ewe and 9–11 days in the doe. Dosages used in the ewe are high as compared with the other species: 20 mg PGF_2-α or 250 μg cloprostenol appear to give the most satisfactory results. In does, 8–15 mg PGF_2-α or 62.5 μg cloprostenol should give good results, with fertility similar to untreated does mated

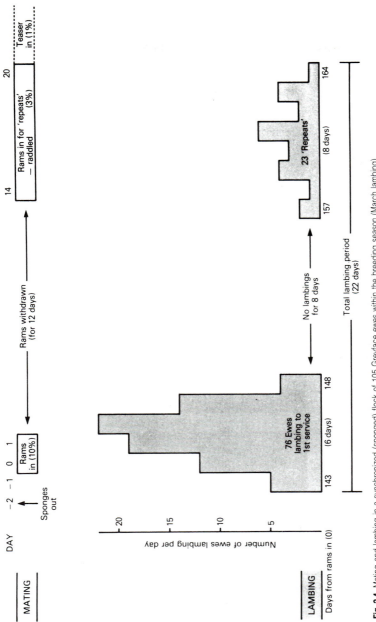

Fig. 2.4 Mating and lambing in a synchronized (sponged) flock of 105 Greyface ewes within the breeding season (March lambing).

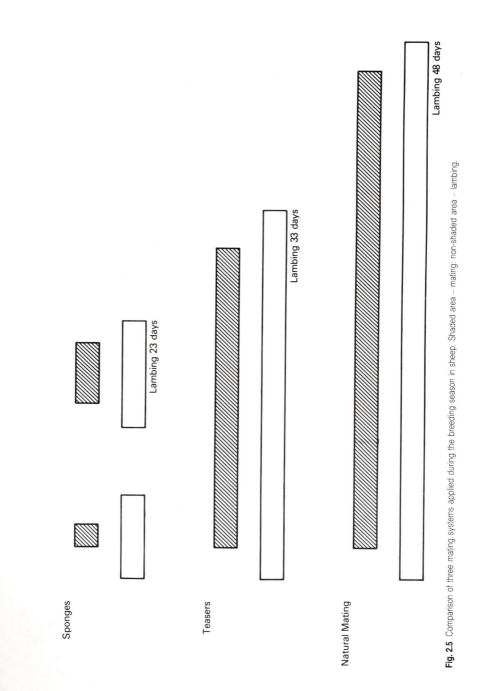

Sponges

Lambing 23 days

Teasers

Lambing 33 days

Natural Mating

Lambing 48 days

Fig. 2.5 Comparison of three mating systems applied during the breeding season in sheep. Shaded area – mating: non-shaded area – lambing.

Table 2.4 Mating timetable and lambing performance in a flock of 300 Suffolk cross Greyface ewes in Gloucestershire, 1982–83.

Mating	
24 August	Ram and teaser testing
1 September	Teasers put in flock
21 September	Teasers removed. Sponges* inserted
4 October	Sponges removed
6 October	Rams put in (10 %) and observed
8 October	Rams removed
20 October	Teasers reintroduced
Lambing (March 1983)	
Ewes given sponges	300
Ewes lambing to first service	257 (86 %)
Lambs born	449 (175 %)

Lambing was completed in six days; 66 % ewes lambed in 60 hours (days 146–148)

*Veramix; Upjohn.
Data from C. Watson (1983) (unpublished).

naturally during the breeding season.

It should be remembered that prostaglandins are prescription-only medicines which should not be handed out to clients for this purpose. Their use is therefore likely to be restricted because of this and also because sponges give equally good or better results and can be supplied to the farmer for application to his or her own stock after veterinary instruction.

INDUCTION OF LAMBING AND KIDDING

When a tighter schedule for lambing than even sponges can provide is desired, induction of lambing can be employed. The problem of retained placenta (as is seen in a high proportion of induced cattle) is not encountered in sheep and the procedure works well.

Betamethazone and dexamethazone at 8–16 mg are most commonly used at 142–144 days of parturition with the majority of lambings occurring from 36–48 hours after treatment (the higher dose rate giving the most reliable results). Oestradiol benzoate at 15–20 mg will produce similar results, and whilst it is suggested that ewes may milk better than following corticosteroid treatment, there may be more dystocia and periparturient lamb losses.

In the ewe, progesterone is produced from the placenta and therefore prostaglandins are ineffective for the induction of parturition.

Unlike the ewe, maintenance of pregnancy in the doe is dependent throughout on progesterone from the corpus luteum. Prostaglandins may therefore be used to initiate parturition providing accurate mating dates are known, and this is important whatever method is used. For example, 20 mg of PGF_2-α given on day 144 of pregnancy will induce kidding between 24 and 36 hours after treatment. If the dose is reduced the interval from injection to parturition is extended. Treatment is most appropriate within five or six days of the mean parturition date for the breed.

Corticosteroids can be used in the doe using similar dosages and timings to those used in the ewe. There would appear to be a longer interval from treatment to parturition using corticosteroids as compared with prostaglandins.

PHOTOPERIOD CONTROL AND MELATONIN

Methods for controlling the breeding season by manipulating the day length in sheep and goats have largely been abandoned due to their impracticability and expense. However, workers in California have successfully brought forward kidding by some two months by using a technique which subjects does to extended day length, thereby obviating the need to lightproof buildings (Bon Durant et al., 1981).

Melatonin, a hormone secreted from the pineal gland at the base of the brain, which is released in response to the onset of darkness, can be used to induce oestrus and ovulation a few weeks earlier than is normal for the breed. This is a natural and more practical alternative to photoperiod control and may be used in place of teasers, or sponges plus PMSG, to advance oestrus during the transition period. To date no commercial product is available in the UK, but trials of synthetic forms of melatonin have shown promise, although fertility following treatment by bolus, or implant, has varied considerably.

CONCLUSIONS

Clients should be advised to use techniques which manipulate the breeding season only after thorough consultation, including an economic appraisal. If they are to be successful they must be fully understood and in particular the high standards of husbandry required must be appreciated.

ACKNOWLEDGEMENT

The author thanks the Upjohn Company for permission to reproduce the illustrations showing the use of the sponges.

REFERENCES AND FURTHER READING

Boland, M. P. & Gordon, I. (1979). *Journal of Agricultural Science, Cambridge* **92**, 247.
Bon Durant, R. H., Darien, B. J., Monro, C. J., Stabenfeldt, G. H. & Wang, P. (1981). *Journal of Reproduction and Fertility* **63**, 1.
Crighton, Haynes, Foxcroft & Lamming (eds) (1978). *Control of Ovulation.* Butterworths, London.
Gordon, I. (1983). *Controlled Breeding in Farm Animals.* Pergamon, Oxford.
Haresign, J. (ed.) (1983). *Sheep Production.* Butterworths, London.
Henderson, D. C. (1987). Manipulation of the breeding season in goats – a review. In *Proceedings of the Goat Veterinary Society*, Vol. 8, No. 1.
Jones, Robertson & Lightfoot (eds) (1979). *Sheep Breeding.* Butterworths, London.
White, I. R. & Russel, A. J. F. (1984). *In Practice* **6**, 200.

CHAPTER 3

Nutrition of the Pregnant Ewe

ANGUS RUSSEL

INTRODUCTION

In theory it should not be difficult to ensure that ewes are properly fed throughout pregnancy. There is now a considerable body of information on the nutrient requirements of the pregnant ewe; allowances expressed in terms of metabolizable energy, rumen degradable protein, undegradable dietary protein, macro-elements, trace elements and vitamins are all well documented for ewes of different breeds and bodyweights.

There is abundant information on the nutrient composition of a wide range of common and exotic feedingstuffs and analytical facilities for determining the nutritive value of conserved forages and purchased concentrates are readily available. Yet, despite this wealth of soundly based information, difficulties still arise in practice in deciding whether ewes are being fed at a level appropriate to their particular stage of pregnancy.

TRANSLATING SCIENCE INTO PRACTICE

These difficulties arise for a variety of reasons. For example, published tables of nutrient requirements generally apply to housed ewes and the estimates of the factor by which these should be increased to take account of the costs of climate and locomotion vary from perhaps 10 to 100 %. Even if confident estimates of these costs can be made, how can the nutrients obtained from the grazing of sparse winter pastures be assessed?

Nutrient requirements are clearly related to the level of production and while this can be measured fairly readily in lactating dairy cows, the "production" of pregnant ewes in terms of the number of foetuses carried is generally not known. Variations in liveweight and body condition, in foetal numbers and in spread of gestational age within a flock also complicate the question. Should the nutritional management of the flock be designed for the average ewe or should it cater for the more productive individuals and those at the more advanced stages of pregnancy? What safety margins should be allowed?

TOWARDS A PRACTICAL SOLUTION

At least some of these questions can be answered by considering the balance between nutrient requirements and nutrient intake – i.e. the extent to which intake satisfies requirements – and how this may be assessed in practice, rather than by attempting to estimate the separate factors of requirement and intake.

First, however, the question of whether requirements and intake should equate exactly must be examined. There is now ample evidence to show that for the greater part of pregnancy nutrient intake can be somewhat lower than the amounts needed to meet in full the requirements for ewe maintenance, wool production, the growth and development of all the products of conception and the development of mammary tissue.

It is not necessary, nor in most circumstances would it be

economic, to supply these requirements in full. Provided that ewes have adequate body reserves of fat and protein at the beginning of pregnancy, a moderate and controlled dependence on these reserves need not have any biologically significant effects on production in terms of lamb birth weight, viability or subsequent growth rate. It then remains to establish what constitutes an acceptable nutrient deficit at any particular stage of pregnancy and how this can best be measured.

BODY CONDITION AT MATING

The nutrition of the ewe during the weeks before mating is an important topic in its own right. For present purposes it is sufficient to state that ewes must be in good body condition at mating to ensure a near optimum ovulation rate and the provision of adequate body reserves on which to draw during pregnancy. "Good condition" at mating means a body condition score of 3.5 in most cases, although in some situations, such as hill flocks, a score of 3.0 may be acceptable.

EARLY PREGNANCY

During the first month of pregnancy when implantation is taking place attention to nutrition can help to minimize the extent of the inevitable embryonic mortality which occurs at this stage of gestation. Ideally ewes should maintain liveweight and body condition during this time. Severe undernourishment, even of very short duration, as can occur in the first of the winter's snow storms, can cause an increased rate of embryo loss. There is also evidence to show that excessively high levels of nutrition at this time can likewise lead to poorer reproductive performance.

Ewes are generally at pasture during early pregnancy and in many cases, particularly in the later lambing hill flocks, herbage quality is insufficient to provide a maintenance level of nutrition and thus the ideal of steady weight and condition is unrealistic.

Supplementary feeding is rarely provided at this stage of pregnancy and in practice a mild degree of undernourishment is unlikely to have any measurably detrimental effects in ewes which were in good body condition at mating. The avoidance of abrupt changes in nutrition during early pregnancy is probably of greater importance than the actual level of feeding.

The adequacy of nutrition in early pregnancy can be monitored in terms of change in either liveweight or body condition. While maintenance of both should remain the ideal, a loss of about 3 % of liveweight or 0.25 of a condition score is generally regarded as acceptable providing that the rate of loss is gradual.

MID PREGNANCY

The important feature of the second and third months of pregnancy is the growth of the placenta which is fully developed by about day 90. The nutrient requirements for the growth of the placenta and other products of conception are relatively modest and can readily be met from a feeding regime which necessitates the controlled catabolism of body reserves. Ewes in good condition (condition score 3.0–3.5) at the beginning of the second month of gestation can be allowed to lose weight and condition during mid pregnancy (i.e. during the following two months) without risk to their subsequent performance. Indeed, there is growing evidence that too high a level of feeding at this time, or even the maintenance of a very high body condition, can lead to reductions in lamb birth weight.

Changes in the weight of the gastrointestinal contents and the increasing mass of the conceptus (particularly the placenta and uterine fluids), make it difficult to interpret alterations in ewe bodyweight during mid pregnancy. Generally, however, a net weight loss of between 2 and 4 kg (depending on the size of the ewe) would be acceptable over this period.

Change in condition score is, at this stage, a more reliable index of the adequacy of nutrition than change in liveweight. A loss of 0.5 of a condition score is perfectly acceptable in ewes in good condition at the beginning of this period and in many cases a loss of up to 0.75 of a score would not be harmful. The objective of the feeding regime at this time should be to ensure a sustained mild degree of undernutrition and to avoid any sudden changes in feeding or periods of severe undernourishment, even short ones.

Correct feeding during mid pregnancy will bring ewes to a condition score of 2.5 to 3.0 at about day 90 of gestation. Those which for one reason or another failed to achieve the desired level of body condition at mating should be fed to restrict the rate of loss. Conversely ewes which were excessively fat at mating (condition score 4 or greater) will benefit from a lower level of feeding such as will reduce condition by at least 0.75 of a score. Overfat ewes are more likely to show inappetence in the later stages of pregnancy and as a result are more susceptible to pregnancy toxaemia.

LATE PREGNANCY

Approximately 70 % of the birth weight of a lamb is gained during the final 30 % (six weeks) of gestation. Nutrition during the last two months of pregnancy is thus clearly of importance in determining lamb birth weight and, through this, lamb viability and subsequent growth rate. However, levels of feeding which supply less than the full nutrient requirements, and which consequently demand further depletion of body reserves, can still result in very acceptable levels of production. In practice nutrition during late pregnancy is a matter of achieving a compromise in which economies of feeding have to be balanced against excessive reductions in lamb birth weight. If the correct balance is achieved the resulting degree of undernutrition will be only moderate and a long way removed from that likely to predispose the animals to pregnancy toxaemia.

Liveweight change as an index of the adequacy of nutrition in late pregnancy can be difficult to interpret because of the rapid increase in foetal weight taking place at this time. As a general rule, however, an acceptable level of feeding over the final eight weeks of gestation will result in increases in ewe bodyweight of about 10 % in ewes with single foetuses and some 18 % in ewes carrying twins.

Body condition scoring is a more useful means of assessing

nutritional adequacy as, unlike liveweight, the measurement itself is not affected by foetal numbers. Ewes within the prescribed condition score range of 2.5–3.0 eight weeks before lambing can afford to lose up to a further 0.5 of a score by parturition. Lambing, however, does not signify the end of the period of dependence on body reserves and it is important that ewes have sufficient reserves left on which to draw during the early weeks of lactation. All ewes should be condition scored about eight weeks before the beginning of lambing and the leaner animals taken out for preferential feeding. No ewes should be in a condition score less than 2.0 at lambing.

Acceptable patterns of condition score change during the different stages of pregnancy and from two initial levels of body condition are illustrated in Fig. 3.1.

USE OF BLOOD METABOLITES IN MONITORING NUTRITIONAL ADEQUACY

A major limitation to the use of changes in liveweight or condition score as indices of the adequacy of nutrition during

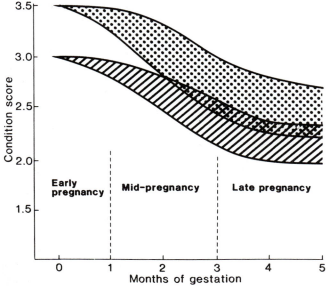

Fig. 3.1 Acceptable patterns of change in body condition score during early, mid and late pregnancy for ewes in condition score 3.0 or 3.5 at mating.

late pregnancy is that they provide information only in hindsight. By the time an inadequate weight gain or an excessive loss of condition has been recognized, an irreparable production penalty may have been incurred. A more immediate assessment of the adequacy of contemporary nutrition is afforded by the measurement of circulating concentrations of certain metabolites, such as plasma glucose, non-esterified or free fatty acid and ketone concentrations. Of these, the plasma concentration of β- or 3-hydroxybutyrate (3-OHB) (one of the two principal ketone bodies) is probably the metabolite best suited to the flock situation. It is less affected by extraneous factors associated with handling and blood sampling than are the other parameters, and the technique has been shown to work well in practice.

TARGETS FOR PLASMA 3-HYDROXYBUTYRATE

In individually fed ewes, which are perhaps encountered only in research institutes, a plasma 3-OHB concentration of 1.1 mmol/litre would be regarded as characterizing an acceptable nutritional deficit which would be expected to reduce lamb birth weight by only about 8 %. If, however, a concentration of 1.1 mmol/litre were to be applied as a target mean concentration for a flock of ewes the inevitable variation around this mean value would be such that a proportion of the ewes would be undernourished to an unacceptable degree. The ewes at the higher end of the range would, of course, be those carrying the greater number of foetuses, which can least afford to be put at risk.

It has been found that in a flock with the normal variation in gestational age and number of foetuses a target mean plasma 3-OHB concentration of 0.8 mmol/litre gives an acceptable distribution of individual values and satisfactory lambing.

When mean plasma 3-OHB concentrations are in excess of this target value the additional feeding required to bring the concentration back to 0.8 mmol/litre can be calculated from the information presented in Fig. 3.2a. For example, in a flock of ewes averaging 60 kg liveweight and with a mean 3-OHB concentration of 1.3 mmol/litre the energy intake should be increased by 2.9 MJ metabolizable energy per ewe per day. This could be met by feeding an additional 260 g of an 86 %

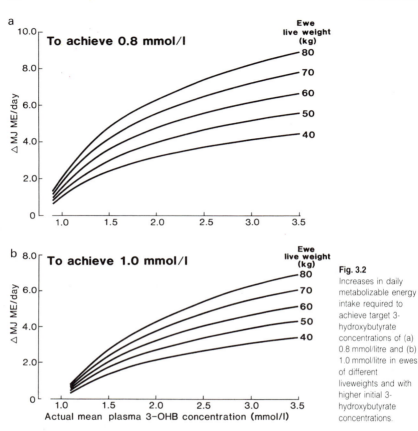

Fig. 3.2
Increases in daily metabolizable energy intake required to achieve target 3-hydroxybutyrate concentrations of (a) 0.8 mmol/litre and (b) 1.0 mmol/litre in ewes of different liveweights and with higher initial 3-hydroxybutyrate concentrations.

dry matter concentrate mixture with a metabolizable energy concentration of 12.9 MJ/kg dry matter.

It is not, however, sufficient only to return the mean 3-OHB concentration to the prescribed target of 0.8 mmol/litre. Provision must also be made to maintain the prescribed moderate degree of undernourishment by making further increases in feeding to match the increase in demands of the growing foetus or foetuses. The amount of feeding required to meet foetal demands can be calculated from the information presented in Fig. 3.3. For example, if the 60-kg ewes are four weeks from lambing and are considered to be carrying twin foetuses it can be estimated that each week the energy requirement of the ewe will increase by about 0.75 MJ metabolizable energy/day. This is equivalent to almost 70 g of the

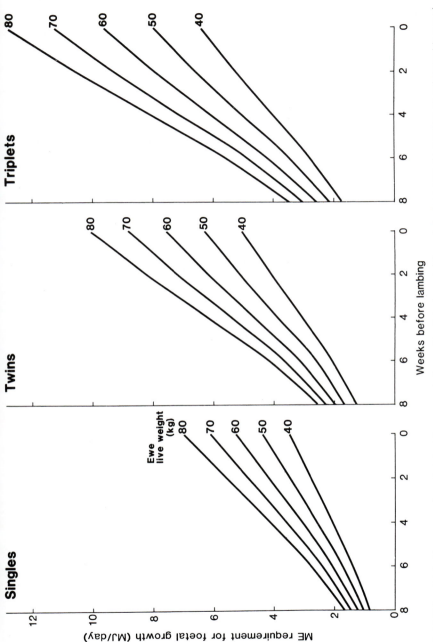

Fig. 3.3 Daily metabolizable energy requirements during late pregnancy for the growth and development of the products of conception (i.e. excluding ewe maintenance) in ewes of different liveweights and carrying single, twin or triplet foetuses.

concentrate. In practice the feed intake could be increased by, say, 120 g/head/day in one week's time and by a further 150 g/head/day two weeks after the first increment.

TOWARDS MEETING FLOCK REQUIREMENTS

A closer degree of control over nutrition in late pregnancy can be achieved by dividing the flock into groups of ewes with similar nutritional requirements. On some farms this will not be possible, but if it can be achieved it will result in better management and more efficient use of expensive feedingstuffs. Until recently the only criteria for dividing the flock into different feeding groups were the expected date of lambing (based on the use of ram harnesses and crayons at mating), body condition (to give lean ewes preferential treatment) and sometimes age (feeding, say, the youngest age group more generously).

With the advent of real-time ultrasonic scanning to determine foetal numbers it is now possible to group ewes for feeding according to the number of foetuses carried, thus giving the ability to regulate feeding with more precision and confidence to the needs of separate groups of ewes.

Where the flock can be divided according to foetal numbers and, in some cases, expected date of lambing, the variation in nutritional state within any group will be considerably reduced. It is then realistic to consider regulating intake to achieve a higher target mean 3-OHB concentration of, say, 1.0 mmol/litre. Amounts of food required to move 3-OHB concentrations from the observed level to the 1.0 mmol/litre target can be calculated from the information contained in Fig. 3.2b.

Taking the example of 60-kg ewes with an actual 3-OHB concentration of 1.3 mmol/litre, the increased energy intake required to reduce it to 1.0 mmol/litre would be approximately 1.4 MJ metabolizable energy/day, equivalent to about 125 g concentrates/head/day. This is less than half the amount of feeding required to achieve the target concentration of 0.8 mmol/litre and represents a saving of more than 5.5 kg concentrates per ewe over a six-week feeding period, or 7.5 kg over eight weeks. In addition, the identification by scanning of the non-pregnant ewes will result in further savings in feed costs and in simpler management.

To summarize, the adequacy of nutrition in early and mid pregnancy can be assessed satisfactorily by monitoring changes in liveweight and/or body condition score.

In the first month the objective should be to maintain the body condition score of 3.0–3.5 set as a target at mating. During the second and third months a level of nutrition which results in a loss in condition of 0.5 of a score would be considered desirable.

A loss of a further 0.5 condition score in late pregnancy would likewise be acceptable but, because of the time taken to detect meaningful changes in condition score, measurement of plasma 3-OHB concentration offers a more immediate means of assessing the adequacy of nutrition at this time. In dealing with flocks in which there is a wide range of gestational age and foetal number a target mean 3-OHB concentration of 0.8 mmol/litre will ensure that the ewes with the higher foetal requirements are not excessively undernourished.

Where flocks can be divided into groups of ewes according to foetal number and stage of pregnancy a higher target mean 3-OHB concentration of 1.1 mmol/litre can safely be set.

FURTHER READING

Meat and Livestock Commission (1983). *Feeding the Ewe*, 2nd edn. MLC, Bletchley.

Robinson, J. J. (1983). *Nutrition of the Pregnant Ewe, in Sheep Production* (ed. W. Haresign). Butterworths, London.

Russel, A. J. F. (1984). *In Practice* **6**, 91.

CHAPTER 4

Determination of Foetal Numbers in Sheep by Real-Time Ultrasonic Scanning

I. R. WHITE and A. J. F. RUSSEL

INTRODUCTION

The ability to determine the number of foetuses carried by pregnant ewes is potentially of considerable benefit to the flockmaster. Advantages include the early identification of non-pregnant ewes with consequent savings in feeding costs and the opportunity to sell these animals advantageously at a time when ewe mutton prices are at a maximum.

It also provides the opportunity to regulate late pregnancy feeding more closely to the requirements of ewes which can be grouped according to the number of foetuses carried, thus achieving further economies in the use of expensive feedingstuffs. The closer control of late pregnancy nutrition can be expected to lead to increased birth weights of multiples and fewer overweight single lambs and, through these effects, to reduced levels of lamb mortality. Feeding in relation to individual requirements is also likely to reduce the incidence of metabolic disorders such as pregnancy toxaemia and thus result in reductions in ewe mortality.

The division of the flock into barren, single-, twin- and triplet-bearing ewes, whether on the hill, in fields or in the inwintering house, also makes for easier management at lambing time.

TECHNIQUES FOR DETERMINING FOETAL NUMBERS

Of the techniques available for determining foetal numbers in pregnant ewes, real-time ultrasonic scanning is the most accurate and rapid.

The use of instruments based on the Doppler principle has been examined by a number of workers but the accuracy and rate of scanning have generally been disappointing. For example, Japanese workers have reported that working at a rate of about 12 ewes per hour some 25 % of ewes diagnosed as carrying single foetuses produced twins. Radiological techniques give higher levels of accuracy but cannot be used effectively before about 80 days of gestation and require the use of very expensive equipment.

Real-time ultrasonic scanning, however, can be used from about 50–100 days of gestation with an accuracy of determination of actual foetal numbers of 97 % and at a rate of more than one ewe per minute. It is also safer to both animal and operator than radiological techniques.

REAL-TIME ULTRASONIC IMAGING

In real-time ultrasonic scanning a transducer containing a linear array of piezoelectric crystals is moved over the ewe's abdomen and the echoes of ultrasound reflected from tissue interfaces lying beneath the transducer are displayed "live" on a screen.

A typical instrument with a 3.5 MHz transducer emits a scanning beam of ultrasound covering a width of 80–100 mm and giving images on the screen of tissue interfaces to a depth of some 200 mm. Unlike radiographic techniques which compress three dimensions into two, the real-time images portray information from only two dimensions, as if the ewe had been sectioned in the plane of the beam of emitted ultrasound and the viewer is looking on to a 80 × 200 mm portion of the cut surface.

Still photographs of images, such as those reproduced in Fig. 4.1, can be difficult to interpret. In practice, however, the ability to alter the angle or position of the transducer and the fact that the image is live, showing the movement of a beating foetal heart, the pulsing of the umbilicus or the kicking of a limb, enables the operator to build a clear mental three-dimensional picture of the tissues being examined.

The interpretation of real-time images is not only a matter of recognizing movement and characteristic shapes. The volume of the fluid-filled areas of the uterus, the "shadows" cast by foetal skulls and scapulae and the characteristic striated shadowing from rib cages all provide the operator with valuable pieces of information. With experience the operator forms an impression of the number of foetuses carried by the ewe being examined within a few seconds, and can then spend a further 15–20 seconds confirming or refuting that initial impression.

SCANNING INSTRUMENTS

There are now several real-time ultrasonic scanning instruments on the market. Most are in the price range of around £6000 to £7000 and are capable of giving the high-resolution images required for the accurate determination of foetal number.

The criteria to be borne in mind when considering the merits of different instruments include the facility to depict a clear distinction between bone, soft tissue and fluid. In some models in which the image has been electronically manipulated useful information such as shadowing from bone can be lost.

In the instruments best suited to present requirements fluid-filled areas of the uterus appear as almost completely black, and bony structures are seen as bright white and casting well-defined shadows. The images should extend to a depth of 190–200 mm and be of high resolution throughout that depth.

Most instruments now available were designed originally for hospital use with human subjects and were not intended to be used under farm conditions on perhaps 100,000 sheep over the course of three or four scanning seasons. Portability and robustness of construction of both the instrument and

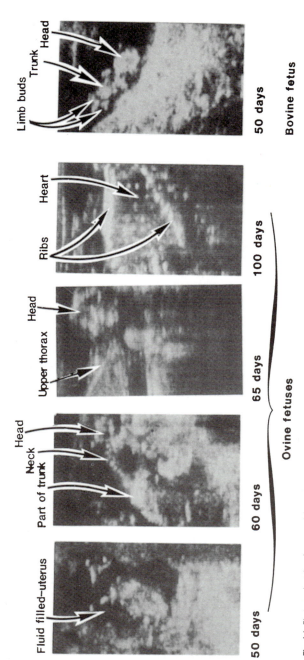

Fig. 4.1 Photographs taken from a real-time ultrasonic scanner screen showing four single ovine foetuses at gestation and one bovine foetus taken from an intrarectal scan.

the transducer should thus be considered in assessing the respective merits of different models.

Some instrument suppliers offer a relatively intensive course of instruction in the use of their equipment to determine foetal numbers in pregnant ewes. In our experience this has proved invaluable to operators unfamiliar with the technique and is certainly advisable for the attainment of the necessary high degree of skill and proficiency.

STAGE OF GESTATION

With this technique pregnancy can be confidently diagnosed from 30 days of gestation or earlier from the imaging of a fluid-filled uterus. However, ewes should not be handled until after 40 days' gestation because of the risk of early embryonic death.

By 35–40 days cotyledons are easily recognized and from about 45–50 days individual foetuses can be detected and counted accurately. The photographs in Fig. 4.1 show how the development of foetuses can be traced over the mid-pregnancy period.

After about 100 days of gestation the size of individual foetuses is such that the image of a cross-section of foetal thorax or abdomen almost fills the screen. That, and the close juxtaposition of individual foetuses within the uterus, make it more difficult to determine foetal numbers quickly and accurately in the final six weeks of gestation. If determinations have to be made during this period these are most readily carried out by counting foetal hearts.

In practice, however, there should be little need to scan ewes beyond 100 days of gestation as any action in the form of nutritional management to be taken as a result of a knowledge of foetal numbers should be implemented at about that stage.

While there is a period of some 50–60 days during which foetal numbers can be readily and accurately determined in any individual ewe, the normal spread of gestational age within a flock reduces the optimum scanning interval to a period from about 11 or 12 to 15 weeks after the beginning of mating.

ANIMAL PREPARATION AND HANDLING

There are now a number of operators scanning pregnant ewes commercially on a contract basis and who have probably developed their own system of handling the animals.

The first requirement in the preparation and presentation of ewes for scanning is that the wool is removed from an area of the abdomen extending for about 200 mm anterior to the udder and the full width of the ventral surface. For scanning the ewe is held on its back, in a semi-recumbent position, or alternatively placed in a cradle similar to a deck-chair so that the lower abdomen is exposed and the operator can move the transducer freely over the area above the uterus. The attachment of the scanning operator's chair to the cradle or other restraining device acts as an anchor and ensures that the ideal location of the animal in relation to the operator and instrument is maintained (Fig. 4.2).

A more sophisticated handling system has been developed recently. In this the ewes proceed up a ramp to an elevated race from which they are turned manually into one of three cradles. While the first cradle is being loaded the ewe in the second cradle is being prepared by shearing the abdomen and the ewe in the third cradle is being scanned. The cradles are then rotated horizontally through 120° during which movement the third ewe is automatically released and the

Fig. 4.2
Scanning in operation, using purpose-built handling equipment.

next ewes are brought to the shearing and scanning positions.

Where the objective of scanning is merely to diagnose pregnancy, as opposed to discovering foetal numbers, accurate results can be obtained without removing any wool by applying the transducer to the bare areas in the groin on either side of the udder. From these positions it is possible to obtain an image of the uterus sufficient to make a confident diagnosis of pregnancy.

CONTACT BETWEEN EWE AND TRANSDUCER

Ultrasound will not travel through air and to ensure good contact between the transducer and the skin surface it is necessary to use an acoustic coupling medium. In theory water should serve the purpose of conducting the ultrasound into the ewe, but in practice it runs off the greasy surface of the abdomen too quickly. Proprietary gels and other agents such as vegetable oil give very satisfactory results on a shaved abdomen. The use of a normal shearing handpiece with a no. 3 comb leaves a sufficient stubble of wool to hold the conducting oil or gel without trapping any air.

Gas inside the ewe is as poor a conductor of ultrasound as is air trapped in the fleece. Problems of poor image quality caused by the intrusion of parts of the digestive tract distended with gas into the area to be scanned can be avoided by withholding food, particularly bulky roughages such as hay, for at least eight hours before scanning.

SCANNING TECHNIQUE

It is important to ensure that the entire uterus is examined. This is most readily achieved by adopting a systematic scanning procedure beginning in the groin area on the further side of the animal, moving forward until the limits of that uterine horn are reached, backwards towards the mid-line, and thus proceeding to the near side, searching the whole area in a zig-zag pattern without lifting the transducer off the ewe (Fig. 4.3).

The same foetus can be readily seen from more than one position and, if the transducer is not kept in contact with the skin throughout the scan, the probability of viewing one foetus twice from different angles and thus making a wrong determination is increased.

SOURCES OF ERROR

If the technique is to find acceptance in the industry it is essential that operators achieve and maintain high levels of accuracy. The most common error in scanning is a failure to detect one of two or more foetuses.

The classification of a multiple-bearing ewe as carrying only a single foetus can have serious consequences if the purpose of using the technique is to regulate late pregnancy nutrition according to foetal numbers. The failure to detect the third or fourth foetuses in multiple-bearing ewes is less serious and in many instances the classification of ewes as non-pregnant, single-bearing and multiple-bearing will be all that is requested by the flockmaster.

Errors of underestimation of foetal number can be overcome only by attention to scanning technique and in particular by

Fig. 4.3
The hand-held transducer is moved over the shorn area of the abdomen immediately above the uterus.

a thorough examination to the limits of both uterine horns.

Errors of overestimation can also occur, as indicated above, by viewing a particular foetus from more than one position. Again this can be minimized only by careful attention to technique. Occasionally however, foetal death, followed by partial or complete resorption, can be the reason for an overestimation of foetal number. Most embryonic and foetal mortality occurs before the stage of gestation at which ewes are likely to be scanned, but a small proportion of losses beyond that point is inevitable. Evidence of these late deaths can be found by careful examination of the placenta at parturition.

An important point to be borne in mind is that because the objective of scanning ewes is generally to determine the number of foetuses carried by individual animals and not to estimate the lambing percentage of the flock as a whole, errors of underestimation and overestimation are cumulative and do not cancel each other out.

RATE OF SCANNING

In commercial scanning operations a high rate of throughput is obviously desirable, although this must never be at the expense of accuracy. In our experience most operators can scan accurately at a rate of about 25 ewes per hour following a two-day course of instruction on the use of the instrument and the interpretation of images. With experience this rate increases relatively quickly to around 80–100 ewes per hour at which point some other factor, such as the preparatory clipping of the presentation of ewes to the operator, becomes limiting.

OTHER APPLICATIONS OF ULTRASOUND SCANNING

Except for the small proportion of intensively managed flocks which produce out of season lambs, the scanning of ewes is likely to be confined to a relatively short season of 3–4 months per year. The equipment can, however, be used to diagnose pregnancy and determine foetal numbers in other species. It is very useful with goats and is probably the surest means of identifying the false pregnancies which can be troublesome in this species.

The same equipment can be used on dogs and the authors have also used the technique succesfully in red deer. With a slim transducer specially designed for intrarectal use it can be used in cattle and horses from about 30 days or less of gestation.

UPDATE

Since the publication of the original report in 1984 there has been a very rapid uptake of the technique by the UK sheepfarming industry. This has been aided to a significant extent by the development of a "sector scanner" (marketed as the "Oviscan 3" or its variant the "Vetscan 2" by BCF Technology Ltd, Livingston, Scotland) suitable for on-farm use.

Instead of an 8–10 cm linear array of some 60–80 crystals, the sector instrument has only four crystals which rotate beneath a protective shield. These crystals are energized over an arc of 85° or 170°, with a choice of depths of field ranging from 5 to 40 cm. Under normal settings the area visualized at any one time is more than five times greater than is possible with most linear array instruments. In most cases the whole of the area of potential interest can be viewed from a single point of contact on the naturally bare skin immediately in front of the udder. It is therefore not necessary to clip wool from the abdomen.

The great benefit of the sector instrument for sheep scanning is that it allows ewes to be scanned in the standing position and thus affords a considerable advantage in terms of labour and handling equipment over linear array systems.

CHAPTER 5

Feeding Lambs by Stomach Tube

ANDREW EALES

INTRODUCTION

Feeding lambs by stomach tube is probably the most significant advance in lamb care in the last 20 years. The stomach
tube is always indicated when feeding young lambs, especially
young weak lambs. Inhalation of milk, which not infrequently
occurs when weak lambs are bottle-fed, is avoided and there
is little risk of the lamb becoming "human-orientated" and
unwilling to suck its mother.

DESTINATION OF FEED

When the tube is fully inserted the tip lies in the rumen (Fig.
5.1). Feed is thus initially deposited in this organ. However,
this seems of little consequence practically. Attempts to gain
direct entry of the feed into the abomasum via the oesophageal
groove by withdrawing the tip into the thoracic oesophagus
rarely seem to be successful. This procedure also appears
to cause the lamb discomfort, presumably because of the
oesophageal distension so produced.

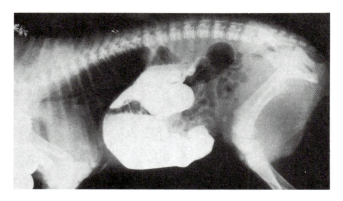

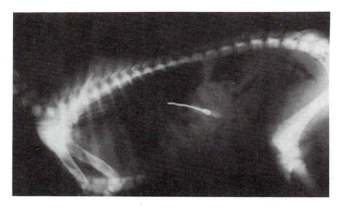

Fig. 5.1
Radiographs of a newborn lamb.
Top: Barium meal given by stomach tube shows the position of the rumen (dorsal) and the abomasum (ventral). The entrance to the abomasum is to the anterior of the organ behind the diaphragm.
Bottom: Stomach tube fully inserted. The tip (outlined by a piece of soft wire) lies in the rumen. (Photographs: Moredun Research Institute).

EQUIPMENT

A number of both rubber and plastic tubes are available. Although plastic tubes have a longer life, my preference is for the soft rubber type which would seem less likely to cause damage in lay hands.

Many tubes are supplied with a funnel-type feed holder. Although these can be effective, they are often the cause of frustration – it's easy to spill the feed and thick colostrum can take an exceedingly long time to drain through the tube. The result is often underfeeding. A 50–60 ml plastic syringe is much more useful.

FEED (Table 5.1)

The ideal regime for a lamb receiving no other milk is ewe colostrum on the first day and milk replacer on the second onwards. Rarely is enough ewe colostrum available for this and cow colostrum can be substituted for all but the first full ewe colostrum feed.

Frozen colostrum should be defrosted carefully and kept in a refrigerator until use. It would be convenient to defrost colostrum in a microwave oven but at present the effects of this procedure on antibody integrity are unknown. Defrosted colostrum has a short shelf-life of 48 hours at maximum. Fresh colostrum should therefore be frozen in small quantities of 250–500 ml.

On rare occasions cow colostrum can cause a severe anaemia. If problems do occur the colostrum from the suspect cow should be discarded. The lamb can be treated by the intraperitoneal injection of 15 ml/kg fresh sheep blood using heparin (5 iu/ml) as anticoagulant. The antibody status of cow colostrum can be improved by prior vaccination of the donor cow (Clarkson *et al.*, 1985).

The concentration of glucose (10 %) in the glucose/electro-

Table 5.1 Feeds for newborn lambs.

Feed	Indication	Problems	Storage
Ewe colostrum	First day	Nutritional scour if fed to older lambs already on milk	12 months in deep freeze (−20°C)
Cow colostrum	First day	Rarely, a severe anaemia. Poor antibody status	12 months in deep freeze (−20°C)
Milk replacer	Second day onwards	Few after first 24 hours. Scour in younger lambs	
Glucose/electrolyte solution (10 % glucose)	Enteric disease – or as an emergency feed		

lyte feed is an estimate. The ideal concentration is unknown
but the glucose content of most "calf scour" preparations
is inadequate for newborn lambs. Prolonged use of these
unsupplemented mixtures can lead to hypoglycaemia and
hypothermia. When treating enteric disease with a glucose/
electrolyte solution a water-soluble antibiotic can be con-
veniently added to the feed.

All feeds should be warmed to blood heat before use.

Lambs require about 50 ml/kg three times daily (all types
of feed). For practical purposes this can be approximated.

Large lamb (single)	250 ml per feed
Medium lambs (twin)	200 ml per feed
Small lambs (triplet)	150 ml per feed

If possible, very small lambs should be fed proportionately
smaller feeds four or five times a day.

TECHNIQUE (Fig. 5.2)

(1) Sit comfortably with the lamb on your lap.
(2) Insert a stomach tube (with no syringe attached) via the
side of the mouth. All but a few centimetres can be easily
introduced into a large lamb.
(3) Watch the lamb for a few seconds. If intratracheal
intubation has been performed the lamb will react extremely
violently. Intratracheal intubation is extremely rare in con-
scious lambs.
(4) Attach the syringe of feed and empty over about 20
seconds.
(5) Remove the empty syringe and continue with further
syringe-fulls until feeding is complete. Feeding is much easier
if the whole feed is pre-syringed.
(6) Gently remove the tube with the final syringe still in
place.

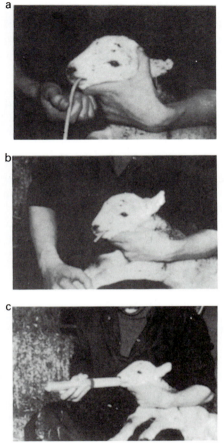

Fig. 5.2
(a) Inserting the tube. (b) The tube in place. (c)
Giving the feed. Note the comfortable position for
both shepherd and lamb.

CONTRAINDICATIONS

The use of the stomach tube in very weak or even unconscious
lambs is not advised. The protective reflexes which prevent
intratracheal intubation, or at least make it very obvious, are
absent. Milk placed in the stomach can be regurgitated and
inhaled. Absorption of nutrients from the gut in collapsed,
normally hypothermic lambs, is very slow. While these lambs
can be safely fed by skilled operators it cannot be generally
advocated. If a shepherd kills one such lamb he or she is

likely to throw the tube away and curse whoever gave it to them. As a practical guide it is safe to feed a lamb by stomach tube if it can lie in sternal recumbency and hold its head up.

PRECAUTIONS

Hygiene in stomach tube feeding is clearly a priority. Ideally the tube should be washed and sterilized after each lamb but under practical conditions this will seldom be possible. As a working compromise, the shepherd can be supplied with two complete sets of feeding equipment. On returning home for a break, the dirty equipment can be left for washing and sterilization and a new set picked up. Dirty equipment should be washed in soapy water and sterilized using a dairy-type hypochlorite disinfectant. Any lamb suffering enteric disease should, of course, be fed last.

Lambs show a remarkable ability to swallow stomach tubes, especially the softer types – don't let go! I am aware of this happening on two occasions – each time no action was taken and the lamb suffered no untoward sequelae.

REFERENCE

Clarkson, M. J., Faull, W. B. & Kerry, J. B. (1985). *Veterinary Record* **116**, 467.

CHAPTER 6

Fostering of Lambs

IAN BAKER

The fostering of orphan lambs or the third lamb of a set of triplets can be a time-consuming and frustrating job. A method using plastic "Elizabethan" dog collars (Buster dog collar size 30; Jorgen Krusse of Marslev, Denmark) has proved to be more successful than other traditional methods such as lamb skinning and stocks (Fig. 6.1).

The collars are easily assembled and fixed around the sheep's neck using a leather dog collar. The plastic must be trimmed

Fig. 6.1

Fig. 6.2

to the end of the nose of each individual sheep to enable it
to graze comfortably. This is easily done when the collar is
fitted (Fig. 6.2).

This type of collar is successful because the ewe is unable
to see or smell the foster lamb. Once the collar is fitted the
ewe and lamb should be kept in a pen for 2–3 days so that
the ewe becomes used to wearing the collar and the lamb is
able to recognize its "mother". The plastic can be numbered
for easy recognition in the field. The collar may remain in
place until weaning.

The only disadvantage appears to be that when the flock is
collected or driven ewes with collars have difficulty seeing the
dog behind them.

ACKNOWLEDGEMENTS

I am indebted to Mrs Rowan Downing who had this idea and
to Mr N. Laurie who took the photographs.

CHAPTER 7

Disbudding and Dehorning of Goats

HUGH BUTTLE, ALAN MOWLEM and ALASTAIR MEWS

INTRODUCTION

The 1982 amendment to the Veterinary Surgeons Act (1966) stipulates that only members of the veterinary profession are permitted to perform disbudding or dehorning of goats and that the subjects must be properly anaesthetized. Those not familiar with the procedure in goats have tended to use techniques and equipment that are commonly used for calves. There are, however, a number of differences and some of the techniques used for calves are not suitable for kids.

The proliferative area at the base of the horn is much more extensive in young goats than it is in calves; thus for successful disbudding a larger area around the base of the horn bud needs to be destroyed. It is not possible to "shell out" the horn bud of kids as it is with calves. In adult goats, the extension of the frontal sinus into the base of the horn is much more prominent than that of cattle, as a result the dehorning of adult goats exposes very large areas of the frontal sinus. There are two nerves that supply the horn base in goats: the cornual branches of the lacrimal nerve supply the lateral and caudal aspects, and a branch from the infratrochlear

nerve supplies the medial and anterior aspects of the horn
(Vitums, 1954).

DISBUDDING OF KIDS

AGE

The horn buds grow extremely rapidly in goats and for
satisfactory results disbudding should be performed when the
kid is 2–7 days old.

ANAESTHESIA

Local anaesthesia

While local anaesthesia is possible for adult goats it tends to
be unsatisfactory for kids. This is partly because of the
diversity of the nerve supply but also because of the dangers
of the local anaesthetic reaching the bloodstream where it may
cause sedation or convulsions.

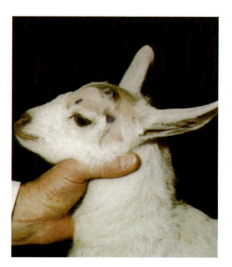

Fig. 7.1
Side view of a kid's head with the two sites for
injection for nerve block marked. (NB General
anaesthesia is recommended for kids.)

General anaesthesia (Table 7.1)

For kids anaesthetized in the surgery, halothane (2–3 %)/ oxygen induced and maintained with an open mask is probably the method of choice. Restraint for induction is easy and recovery is also rapid, with the kids being up and about within 5 minutes of the end of the operation.

When the operation is performed on the farm alphaxalone/al- phadolone, 6 mg/kg bodyweight (Saffan: Glaxo) have been successfully used by intravenous injection. Xylazine, at a dose of 0.3–0.4 mg/kg (Rompun: Bayer) has also been used but care must be taken not to overdose or sedation can be considerably prolonged with the associated dangers of hypothermia and inanition.

A good combination of agents is: atropine 0.2 mg/kg subcut- aneously with xylazine 0.2 mg/kg intramuscularly followed 10 minutes later with ketamine 10 mg/kg intramuscularly; these give good analgesia and insensibility with a reasonable recovery time.

PROCEDURE

The procedure used depends upon the type of disbudding iron available. There are two methods which use either a flat branding iron (recommended by the authors) or a calf dehorning iron.

Table 7.1 List of anaesthetic agents and dose rates for kids.

Agent	Dose
Halothane/oxygen	2–3 %
Alphaxalone/alphadolone (Saffan: Glaxo)	6 mg/kg i.v.
Thiopentone	10 mg/kg i.v.
Xylazine (Rompun: Bayer)	0.3–0.4 mg/kg i.m.
A combination of drugs:	
Atropine	0.2 mg/kg s.c.
Xylazine	0.2 mg/kg i.m.
then Ketamine (10 minutes later)	10.0 mg/kg i.m.

i.v., intravenously; i.m., intramuscularly; s.c., subcutaneously.

Flat branding iron

Three branding irons should be obtained from a local black-smith. The operative ends of these should be flat, 2.2, 2.5 and 2.8 cm in diameter and of sufficient weight to retain heat, i.e. approximately 1.5 cm thick. Before use these irons should be heated to 600°C, i.e. to a dull red colour: a propane gas blow torch is suitable for heating the irons.

Cut off the tip of the horn bud and apply the hot iron to the horn bud. (Fig. 7.2). It is necessary to "rock" the iron around the periphery of the horn bud to ensure that all proliferative tissue, especially at the caudal and lateral aspects, is adequately cauterized over an area considerably larger than the horn bud itself. The iron should be applied to each horn bud for 20–25 seconds in all, and a reheated iron should be used for each bud.

Fig. 7.2
Application of the hot iron to a horn bud. Note the use of general anaesthesia.

Calf dehorning iron

Commercial calf irons can be used, but most are too small in diameter and have a recessed centre which makes destruction of all horn tissue difficult. Commercial irons can sometimes be modified by enlarging the diameter with copper tubing and/or by obliterating the central recess. Again the iron needs to be heated to 600°C.

Apply the iron to the horn bud to give a circular cautery line around the base. Cut out the bud with a scalpel and take an extra 2–3 mm of skin around the base (a large cork borer (25–28 mm diameter) is convenient for this) then use the iron again to cauterize the whole area which should be as extensive as shown in Fig. 7.3.

COMMENTS

Although halothane is not flammable, the high concentration of oxygen used in a gaseous anaesthetic mixture can occasionally support combustion of the hair on a kid's head. This is alarming when it occurs but it is easily quenched without any damage being inflicted.

The area needed to be cauterized on some kids may seem

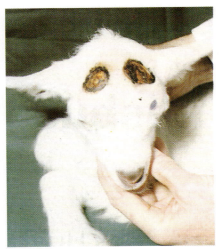

Fig. 7.3
Front view of the kid's head showing adequate destruction of the horn buds. The dot above the left eye is the site of injection for blocking the infratrochlear nerve.

excessive, but it is much better to make a thorough job initially, rather than have to remove misshapen horn regrowth at a later stage.

If attempts are made to remove the horn buds later than a week or so after birth horn regrowth (scurs) may occur, particularly with intact male kids where horn growth is vigorous. The broad base of these small horns makes the cautery more difficult, even after the horn tip has been removed with a scalpel.

If possible, make a point of inspecting the animals about 4–6 months later and note the extent and position of any regrowth of horn, as this indicates areas of incomplete destruction at the time of disbudding.

CAUTIONARY NOTE

There have been a number of reports of cortical necrosis and even burning through the skull as a result of prolonged use of the disbudding iron. This can be prevented by ensuring that the iron is sufficiently hot and then only leaving it on for

Table 7.2 Disbudding of kids – important reminders.

(1)	The best age to disbud a kid is between 2 and 7 days old
(2)	Anaesthesia of such animals needs to be administered with great care – it is easy to overdose
(3)	Kids are very sensitive to the toxic effects of lignocaine, should it reach the bloodsteam
(4)	Kids have relatively very large horn buds (particularly males). Calf disbudders are normally not large enough and so it may be necessary to enlarge the area with a scalpel and recauterize
(5)	Remove protruberant horn bud with a scalpel before applying an iron.
(6)	The iron should be heated to a cherry red colour (600°C)
(7)	Remove anaesthetic mask during disbudding if gas disbudder is used
(8)	When applying the heated disbudding iron, *do not* press too hard or for too long (20–25 seconds maximum)
(9)	Administer tetanus antitoxin/antibiotic as appropriate

the minimum time necessary to remove the bud.

Tetanus antitoxin/antibiotics should be administered where appropriate.

DEHORNING ADULT GOATS

Dehorning adult goats is not without its hazards owing to the very large sinuses which are exposed at the base of the horn. The operation should only be performed in the autumn or winter, when there are no flies around.

ANAESTHESIA

Local anaesthesia

The goat should first be sedated (e.g. xylazine). The cornual branch of the lacrimal nerve is blocked as in the calf, and that of the infratrochlear nerve dorsomedial to the orbit, where it can often be palpated. The needle should be pushed under the skin dorsomedial to the eye, as close as possible to the orbit. A dose of 2–3 ml of 2 % lignocaine at each site is sufficient for an adult goat. The skin at the base of the horn should be tested for desensitization before the horn is removed.

General anaesthesia

A wide variety of general anaesthetics have been used, including xylazine and ketamine, thiopentone and halothane/oxygen.

TECHNIQUE

The skin should be incised 1 cm from the base of the horn. This is particularly important around the caudolateral and caudomedial areas, in order to prevent regrowth of horn. Holding the head firmly, the horn is removed using an obstetric wire saw or a dehorning saw. Haemorrhage from the superficial temporal artery can be severe and should be ligated or cauterized. Because of the large sinuses, particularly in adult males, it is often considered prudent to cut the horns some 2 cm above the base; this unfortunately means that the stumps will continue to grow.

POST-OPERATIVE CARE

A tetanus antitoxin/antibiotic course should be administered. The exposed sinuses will normally close within a few days but in some patients the sinuses may remain open for several months. The wound should be sprayed daily with antibiotic. The head may be bandaged post-operatively, in which case the bandage should be changed after two days. The second bandage may be left on for 5–7 days. Hay should be dampened and fed from the floor and not from a hay rack.

REFERENCE

Vitums, A. (1954). *Journal of the American Veterinary Medical Association* **125**, 284.

CHAPTER 8

Goats for Fibre Production

ANGUS RUSSEL

INTRODUCTION

The current interest in farming fibre-producing goats in the UK is not as new as many suppose. A number of attempts to import "shawl wool" goats from Tibet were made in the eighteenth century, but these failed as a result of disease or shipwreck. Later importations were successful in landing live goats in this country, but most of the animals died shortly afterwards. Those that did survive were regarded largely as curiosities and were not used to establish herds of productive animals from which fibre could be harvested.

This recent renewed interest in goats in general, and fibre-producing goats in particular, stems to a large extent from the current oversupply of many traditional animal products. Livestock farmers faced with surpluses of milk, butter and beef are seeking alternative enterprises and goats are one of a number of such alternatives now being given serious consideration.

BREED TYPES

There are two main types of fibre-producing goats. The first is a distinct breed, the angora, which produces mohair. The fleece comprises a single coat which grows continuously throughout the year.

The second type is the cashmere goat which has a double coat. The fleece is made up of a coarse hairy outer coat which has no commercial value, and a fine undercoat or "down" which is cashmere – one of the most valuable of all animal fibres. This soft undercoat, unlike mohair, grows seasonally, from mid-summer to mid-winter and is shed naturally in late winter or early spring. There is no single distinct breed of cashmere goat, and indeed dairy goats have an undercoat, albeit of negligible amounts, which probably conforms to the definition of cashmere.

Another type of goat fibre which is currently being produced is known as "cashgora". This comes from angora crosses produced mainly from the process of "grading-up" from dairy breeds to "pure" angora through five generations of crossing female progeny with angora bucks. Whether cashgora is a transitory product which will disappear when there is a sufficient number of pure angoras in the country or whether crossbreds will be maintained specifically for cashgora production remains to be established.

To dispel any confusion which may still exist about the nomenclature of animal fibres, it should be noted that the product known as "angora" comes from rabbits and not from goats.

BREED ORIGINS

ANGORAS

Angora goats originated in Turkey and spread from there to South Africa and the United States in the middle of the nineteenth century. These three countries are still the major mohair producers, with most of the US production coming from Texas. Angoras are now more widely distributed and the first importation to the UK this century comprised 19 animals from New Zealand and four from Tasmania which arrived in 1981.

Since then there have been many shipments of live animals and frozen embryos from New Zealand and Tasmania. More recently, animals of Texan ancestry have been imported from Canada and a small number have also been brought in from Holland. Further imports are likely to arrive from European countries within the next few years when herds there have been established for a sufficient period to comply with the UK health protocols.

CASHMERE GOATS

The only known survivors of the early importations of cashmere goats to the UK are the Windsor goats belonging to the Royal Family and a herd on the Great Orme in North Wales which came from the same source. The amount of cashmere presently produced by the animals in these herds is very disappointing, and if at one time their production was high this has been largely lost either through inbreeding or by adulteration through indiscriminate crossing with dairy breeds.

The foundation stock of the embryonic Scottish cashmere production industry is the feral goat (Fig. 8.1). Herds of feral goats have existed in Scotland for many centuries. At one time goats were the most numerous type of domestic livestock

Fig. 8.1
Scottish feral buck.

Fig. 8.2
Icelandic bucks. The
one on the right is
naturally polled.

in parts of Scotland, but with changes in farming systems in the late eighteenth and early nineteenth centuries goats fell out of favour and many were abandoned to augment existing feral herds or form new ones. Animals from these herds, found mainly in the south-west of Scotland and throughout the Highlands and outer islands, and also from herds in Wales and northern England, have recently been redomesticated.

As with angoras, cashmere goats have also recently been brought into the UK. Six goats were imported from Iceland in 1986. Although these are not from a recognized cashmere breed – there are in fact only 200–300 goats in Iceland – these animals appear to have a thicker undercoat than many goats from traditional cashmere-producing countries (Fig. 8.2). Genetic material has also been imported from Tasmania (Fig. 8.3) and New Zealand; frozen semen from Tasmania was brought in in 1986, followed in 1987 by live animals from that same source and frozen embryos from New Zealand. Live animals, frozen semen and further consignments of embryos were imported from New Zealand in late 1987 and early 1988. Frozen embryos have also been imported recently from the USSR.

Fig. 8.3
Tasmanian cashmere yearling buck.

FIBRE CHARACTERISTICS

MOHAIR

Mohair is a long lustrous fibre which on the animal forms characteristic ringlets or curled staples. Although some angora goats are coloured, the vast majority are white and in practice only wholly white animals are retained for breeding.

Annual levels of mohair production vary with sex, age and strain of animal. Typical levels of production from kids are 1–1.5 kg per year while adult does might be expected to produce 2.5–3.5 kg per year. Castrate males and bucks produce higher fleece weights than females, and animals of Texan origin generally produce more than the Australasian strains.

Fibre diameter is an important determinant of price and also varies with age, sex and strain. The finer the fibre, the more valuable it is. A typical mean fibre diameter of superfine kid mohair is around 25 μm or less, while that of strong adult mohair could be 36 μm or more. Mohair from males is generally coarser than that from females.

Mohair is a long and rapidly growing fibre and it is usual to shear the animals every six months when the fleece length is around 120–150 mm. In quoting levels of production there is sometimes confusion between fleece weight (six months' growth) and annual weight of mohair produced. Since rate of fibre growth is greater in summer than in winter, and because animals are not necessarily shorn at exactly six-month intervals, care must be taken in interpreting production figures.

Medullated fibres (fibres with an uninterrupted hollow core) and kemps (very coarse, straight, opaque, chalky white fibres with a latticed medulla) occur to some extent in many angoras and are regarded as a serious fault which causes problems in the processing of mohair and should be selected against in breeding.

The Texan strains of angora are reputed to have fewer medullated fibres and kemps than the Australasian strains, but the fibre has a higher grease content and thus the weight loss on scouring the fleece is greater. The greasier fleece may, however, be an advantage to the animal kept under UK climatic conditions.

CASHMERE

Cashmere is the soft undercoat or "down" carried by double-coated goats. The fibres are non-medullated and are often pigmented, although white (unpigmented) cashmere is preferred by the processors and commands a higher price than grey or brown.

Cashmere is finer than mohair. The highest quality cashmere, such as that imported from China, has a mean fibre diameter of less than 15 μm, while the coarser material imported from Iran and Afghanistan has a mean fibre diameter of 18–19 μm. Fibre diameter and weight of production vary widely with the breed of goat and, to a lesser extent than in mohair, with age and sex of animal.

UK feral goats carry greater quantities of cashmere than any of the dairy breeds, but still in insufficient amounts for commercially viable cashmere production enterprises. Levels of production range from virtually zero to about 200 g per goat with an average of between 80 and 100 g. The quality of their cashmere, however, is very high and, with an average fibre diameter of about 14 μm, is as good as that produced anywhere in the world. The majority of UK feral goats are coloured but this can readily be changed by crossing with white sires.

Cashmere goats have recently been imported to the UK to establish commercial cashmere herds and for use in crossbreeding programmes with feral goats (see below). The quantity and quality of cashmere produced by the imported stock are both highly variable, but the better animals typically produce around 350–400 g of cashmere with a mean fibre diameter of about 17 μm.

BREEDING SYSTEMS

The number of fibre-producing goats in the UK is increasing rapidly and wide use is being made of artificial insemination, superovulation and embryo transfer techniques in both angora and cashmere animals.

ANGORAS

In addition to the multiplication of angora goats by the natural mating of pure stock and through superovulation and embryo transfer, the British Angora Goat Society also recognizes the progency of stock "graded-up" from dairy goats as "pure" angoras. In this system at least five generations of back-crossing to angora bucks is required for registration by the breed society. The establishment of a pure angora herd by this method obviously takes some considerable time and is not necessarily less expensive in the long term than embryo transfer techniques using either purchased frozen embryos or embryos collected directly from a few superovulated donor does.

CASHMERE GOATS

As cashmere goats are a type rather than a single identifiable breed there is no officially recognized grading-up system analogous to the angora, whereby after a fixed number of crossings the progeny are deemed to be "cashmere goats".

A number of approaches to the establishment of commercially viable cashmere-producing herds are being pursued. One starting point is with native feral females which are crossed with superior imported cashmere bucks either by natural service or artificial insemination (Figs 8.4 and 8.5). The female progeny from these matings are in turn crossed with superior bucks. The stage at which commercial quantities of cashmere are produced will depend on the superiority of the bucks used, but substantial progress should be made in two generations. Feral female stock are scarce and as an alternative to the above approach some producers are starting by mating dairy females to feral males. Of the dairy females available the Toggenburg type and British Alpine, which tend to have more of an undercoat than Anglo-Nubian and Saanen type goats, are preferred.

Genetic correlations among cashmere fibre characteristics are such that, unless very rigorous selection is practised, increases in cashmere weight are likely to be accompanied by decreases in quality (i.e. increases in fibre diameter). A

Fig. 8.4
Icelandic × Scottish feral kid

Fig. 8.5
Tasmanian ×
Scottish feral
cashmere kid.

breeding system designed to increase weight of cashmere while safeguarding quality is being operated by Cashmere Breeders Ltd, a body presently comprising nine commercial farmers and the Macaulay Land Use Research Institute. Selected stock, imported as live animals, semen and embryos from Iceland, Tasmania, New Zealand and the USSR are being used to establish a number of lines from which the superior individuals will be used to create an elite herd supplying quality breeding stock to the cooperating herds and ultimately to the wider cashmere producing industry.

MANAGEMENT SYSTEMS

At present only a few of the fibre-producing goats in this country are being managed under conditions in which commercial herds must ultimately operate. The valuable stud animals kept primarily for the production of pedigree breeding stock are not turned out on hill or upland farms to face the rigours of our climate. However, if mohair and cashmere production are to be economically viable, fibre goats must eventually be kept under similar conditions to sheep. Indeed the management of fibre-producing goats will be more akin to that of sheep than that of dairy goats, with kids being suckled by their dams and weaned at about 14 weeks old.

SHELTER

The main and most important difference in the management of sheep and goats is the latter's requirement for shelter. The goat's fleece does not afford the same protection against rain as does sheep's wool and even hardy feral goats should be provided with some form of shelter when they are kept under farm conditions which seldom include topographic shelter.

A number of herds of cashmere goats are being run successfully on hill farms with access to inexpensive home-made shelters comprising three sides and a roof. Such shelters are well used and ideally should be fitted with slatted floors to avoid the otherwise inevitable fouling and poaching, and to ensure the animals have a dry area on which to lie.

There has been less experience in managing herds of angora goats in the harsher parts of the UK, but in view of the dry areas of the world from which this breed come they may be less well suited to being outwintered than are cashmere goats.

FENCING

One of the reasons why goats fell into disfavour as domestic livestock in the late eighteenth and early nineteenth centuries was the difficulty, or perhaps more correctly the near impossibility, of excluding them from arable crops and woodlands. While a dry stone dyke is no more an obstacle to a goat now than it was then, modern fencing materials, and particularly electric fences, ensure that goats can be securely contained. Most goats will respect normal sheep fences unless grazing is in short supply, but the addition of a single electrified wire set about 250 mm high and a similar distance inside the fence will keep in all but the most determined individuals. Such animals are best culled at an early date.

The containment of newly acquired feral stock is not as difficult as might be imagined. Clearly the fencing must be good, but that described above should be adequate if the animals are allowed an opportunity to settle into their new surroundings and are not unduly disturbed or rounded up by dogs until they have become accustomed to their new surroundings and the persons looking after them.

HANDLING FACILITIES

The pens or yards in which routine management operations such as dosing, vaccination, and hoof trimming are carried out, require to be of a higher standard than those generally used for sheep. This is particularly so for feral stock, since goats in general are more agile than sheep and, when closely confined or desirous of avoiding an operation which they dislike, can easily jump standard sheep yard gates and hurdles. The external gates and perimeter of the yard should be 1.5–1.7 m high and preferably without any foothold on the inside. Vertically hung boards are preferable to the traditional pattern of posts and rails.

The area where hoof trimming is to be carried out should ideally be concreted to make cleaning easier and all yards should include a footbath for routine use.

HOUSING

Where for any reason fibre-producing goats have to be housed, the general principles are similar to those for sheep. Goats can be kept in groups of 20–30 with a floor allowance of about 2 m per adult. Divisions between pens should be higher than for sheep and preferably about 1.2 m.

Goats kept in groups quickly establish a social hierarchy and care should be taken to watch for signs of bullying. Animals in any one group should be matched as far as possible for size and weight, and horned and polled individuals should not be mixed. Although goats will eat a wide variety of feedstuffs they are fastidious as regards the cleanliness and freshness of their feed and will not eat material which has fallen from the hay rack on to the floor. Care should be taken in designing hay racks and feed troughs to minimize wastage of food and prevent any possible injury to animals.

Goats are notoriously curious animals and will investigate and chew most things within reach. Electrical fittings and wiring should therefore be located at a height of at least 180 cm and alkathene water pipes should be protected by covering the lagging with, for example, fine securely-bound wire netting.

FIBRE HARVESTING

Mohair is harvested from angora goats by shearing. This is generally a twice-yearly operation carried out in spring and autumn. As mohair grows continuously, any fibre left on the animal will be harvested in the next shearing and it is thus possible to leave a sufficient depth of fibre to afford the animal some protection and insulation without losing production. It may be necessary to house the stock for some time after shearing, depending upon weather conditions, and the level of feeding should be increased following shearing to minimize the risk of cold shock.

In China, the USSR and other traditional cashmere-producing countries, the fibre is harvested by combing in the early months of the year when the cashmere is naturally shed. This is a labour-intensive operation and in New Zealand and Australia cashmere is harvested by shearing. In the UK it is considered that cashmere will generally be harvested by combing, probably in February. Although this may take 15 minutes or more per goat the value of the fibre (£70 per kg for top-quality white cashmere) justifies the expense involved. Research is currently in progress to examine the feasibility of putting coats, designed to contain the cashmere fibres within the guard hairs, on the animal from January to May. Preliminary results indicate that the cashmere can then be combed out in 2–3 minutes. Other work on the endocrinological manipulation of the seasonality of cashmere growth and shedding is also being carried out but no results are available at this stage.

If cashmere is to be harvested by shearing in this country, this would require to be done in January and it would be essential that the animals were housed in suitable accommodation.

While angora and cashmere goats in the UK are being kept principally for their fibre, a substantial proportion of the income from such enterprises will come from the sale of animals, and particularly castrate males, for meat. Angora kids destined for slaughter for meat are likely to be managed in a similar manner to lambs, with animals being sold over a period of weeks or a few months after weaning. In most cases the animals will be shorn before slaughter.

With cashmere goats the first harvest of fibre cannot be taken until at least January or February and it is probable that many kids destined for meat will be kept until after that harvest has been taken.

Goats also have a considerable potential to alter the vegetational composition of sown and indigenous pastures through their grazing preferences which are markedly different from those of sheep and cattle. They are particularly useful for controlling or eliminating weeds, such as rushes, thistles, nettles, etc., and thus improving pasture for the benefit of sheep and cattle production. It is probable that stock which are ultimately to be slaughtered for meat could be used for this purpose as yearlings, gaining further weight inexpensively while improving pasture quality. Such animals can provide good and very acceptable carcases at 18 months old.

INFORMATION SOURCES

Goat fibre production is still in its infancy in this country and many of the new or aspiring entrants to the industry find it difficult to obtain specialist advice. Information can be obtained from the following bodies:

British Angora Goat Society,
Three Counties Agricultural Society,
The Showground,
Malvern,
Worcestershire

The Goat Veterinary Society,
The Limes,
Chalk Street,
Rettendon Common,
Chelmsford, Essex

Disease

CHAPTER 9

Chlamydial Abortion in Sheep

I. D. AITKEN

INTRODUCTION

Chlamydial abortion, also known as enzootic abortion of ewes, is the most commonly diagnosed cause of ovine infectious abortion in Britain. The Veterinary Investigation Service receives about 6000 submissions of material from incidents of sheep abortion annually. Some 25 % of these abortions are attributed to chlamydial infection, 23 % to toxoplasmosis and 12 % to miscellaneous infections. The rest remain undiagnosed.

Enzootic abortion of ewes is caused by ovine strains of the zoonotic microorganism *Chlamydia psittaci* which exhibit a predilection for placental tissue. This highly specialized Gram-negative bacterium has a unique life cycle involving alternate intra- and extracellular phases which confer advantages for evasion of host immune responses and facilitates the maintenance of low-grade asymptomatic infection, usually in the gut. However, pregnancy affords the right circumstances for expression of the selective pathogenicity of *C. psittaci*.

In a severe outbreak of chlamydial abortion, up to one-third of the ewe flock may be affected. In endemic situations figures of 5–10 % are more usual. Chlamydial infection is most commonly introduced into a previously clean flock by sheep carrying an asymptomatic infection. Some of these animals go on to abort and disseminate chlamydiae at that time to in-contact lambs and ewes. Infection is acquired by ingestion resulting in intestinal carriage and faecal excretion of chlamydiae which helps to perpetuate infection within a flock. However, because *C. psittaci* is a common parasite of a wide variety of animals and birds the possibility of occasional inter-species transmission cannot be wholly discounted when considering sources of flock infection.

PRESENTATION

Chlamydial abortion occurs in the last 2–3 weeks of pregnancy without premonitory signs. It results from a progressive necrotizing placentitis that starts in the third month of gestation. As well as abortions, premature or full-term delivery of stillborn, moribund or weak lambs is encountered, although the progeny of some infected ewes may appear healthy. Aborted lambs usually appear fresh and show little or no gross pathology although distension of the abdomen with bloodstained fluid is occasionally evident.

In contrast, the placenta reveals gross lesions involving necrosis and thickening of cotyledons and adjacent intercoty-ledonary tissue (Fig. 9.1). Quantities of a brownish fluid exudate containing particles of tissue debris are often present.

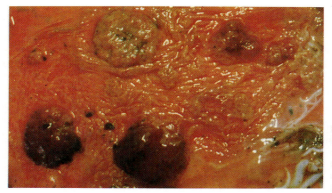

Fig. 9.1
Placentitis caused by *C. psittaci* showing affected cotyledon and thickening of adjacent membrane.

The degree and extent of these changes vary between individuals. Although a minority of aborting ewes may develop a secondary metritis if placental expulsion is incomplete, most are unaffected by the abortion and breed normally the following season.

DIAGNOSIS

Chlamydial abortion is very much a disease of intensively managed sheep, whether housed or lambing outside, and rarely occurs in extensively managed hill flocks. Of the other causes of abortion which must be considered only toxoplasmosis produces specific changes in placental cotyledons. These take the form of tiny white foci in the cotyledons which often stand out against the adjacent bright red tissue. If the foci are numerous their confluence can give cotyledons a necrotic appearance which superficially resembles that seen in enzootic abortion of ewes. However, in toxoplasmosis the intercotyledonary placental membrane is not affected. Discrete placental lesions are not features of abortions caused by infection with bacteria such as *Campylobacter fetus* or *Salmonella* species or in the pestivirus-induced abortion of Border disease.

Confirmation of diagnosis of chlamydial abortion requires microscopic examination of smears from affected areas of placenta (Fig. 9.2). When stained by a modified Ziehl–Neelson

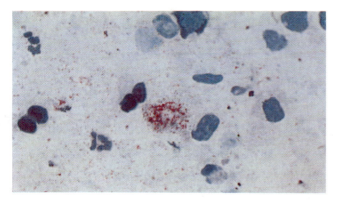

Fig. 9.2
Chlamydial bodies in a stained placental smear.

procedure, numerous chlamydial organisms are seen as minute (0.3 μm) red bodies among blue-staining cell debris. If no placenta is available, smears can be made from vaginal swabs taken within 24 hours of abortion or from the wet fleece of a recently aborted or stillborn lamb. However, fleece smears generally reveal far fewer organisms than those from placenta or vaginal swabs. Though Q fever only rarely causes ewe abortion in Britain it is well to remember that the rickettsia, *Coxiella burnetii*, resembles *C. psittaci* in stained smears. However, the two microorganisms can be distinguished serologically.

If isolation of *C. psittaci* is required, a small piece of affected cotyledon or fresh vaginal swabs should be immersed in a suitable transport medium for despatch to an appropriate laboratory where culture can be attempted.

If necessary, serology may be used for retrospective diagnosis. Paired serum samples taken from a number of animals at the time of abortion and 2–3 weeks later may assist in confirming or refuting a diagnosis of chlamydial abortion. It may also be helpful to have samples from ewes which have lambed normally.

Where possible, diagnostic monitoring should continue throughout lambing as more than one infectious agent may be involved in a flock abortion problem. At least 10 % of abortions occuring over the lambing period should be submitted for laboratory examination.

CONTROL

For any abortion, it is most important to identify affected ewes and to separate them from other sheep until a firm diagnosis has been established and the correct control policy adopted. In enzootic abortion of ewes, vast numbers of infectious chlamydia are shed in the placenta, foetus and uterine discharges. As these materials and fluids are the main sources of infection for susceptible in-contact sheep their prompt removal and destruction must be given priority. A layer of clean bedding should be provided for contaminated lambing pens. Ewes which have aborted or produced stillborn lambs should continue to be isolated at least until their uterine discharges have dried up. Although chlamydiae are not transmitted in milk, aborted ewes should not be used as foster mothers as their close physical contact with adopted lambs heightens the risk of lamb infection.

The foregoing recommendations are particularly applicable in flocks with an extended lambing pattern as there is good evidence that infection and abortion can occur within the same pregnancy. Although infection may be acquired at any stage of pregnancy the placenta seems especially receptive to chlamydiae from about 80–110 days of gestation. Thus, ewes exposed to infection when 3–4 months pregnant are particularly at risk and liable to abort 5–6 weeks later. In such situations consideration can be given to antibiotic therapy with long-acting tetracycline at a dose rate of 20 mg/kg, repeating the injections at 10–14 day intervals until lambing takes place. However, it must be emphasized that while such treatment will moderate the course of infection and reduce the overall incidence of abortion, some ewes will still abort or produce stillborn lambs and infected placentae may occur, which would still act as a source of infection to other ewes. Chemotherapy should be regarded as an emergency measure and not advocated as a routine policy.

PREVENTION

Relevant issues include the future of ewes that have aborted, the source of replacements, vaccination and possible eradication. Although most ewes which have experienced chlamydial abortion are systemically immune and will breed successfully, some are likely to be faecal excretors of *C. psittaci*. Accordingly, retention of aborted ewes in the breeding flock must be questioned unless they can be separately maintained as the nucleus of an immune flock.

Ideally, replacement females should be obtained from sources known to be free from chlamydial abortion. Although the commonly used complement fixation test does not reliably identify individual carrier animals, it is useful in assessing group status. Alternative more sensitive tests, like ELISA, may eventually prove more reliable for this purpose. Similarly, there is promise in a skin test which has been used successfully in experimental and field studies. Based upon comparative delayed hypersensitivity reactions, the test at present requires intrapalpebral inoculation of test and control antigens. Given a satisfactory alternative site the test could have more routine application.

Although there is no direct evidence to implicate tups in the natural transmission of chlamydial infection during breeding it is probably better to avoid using tups from known infected flocks.

The formalin-inactivated vaccine first developed 30 years ago has been modified recently by addition of a representative current field strain of *C. psittaci*. Experimental evidence and field observations have shown that, properly used, both the original and current vaccines will help to prevent chlamydial abortion but do not eliminate infection. Vaccination is only part of the range of control measures to be implemented in dealing with this difficult disease. After an outbreak all retained and replacement females should be vaccinated just before the next tupping, with revaccination after three years or sooner if circumstances warrant it, e.g. when the challenge is likely to be severe or viable progeny have high value. Annually, all new entrants to the breeding flock should be vaccinated. Eradication requires the culling of all ewes known or suspected to be infected and any of their surviving ewe lambs, obtaining of replacement females from a source free of infection and careful monitoring during the ensuing lambing season. Alternatively, if the farm structure allows it and there is strong commitment by the flock owner it may be possible to establish and run two separate flocks, one consisting of aborted and therefore immune ewes and the other a clean, naive flock. The underlying aim is to run down the "infected" flock and build up the clean one.

THE HUMAN RISK

The zoonotic potential of avian strains of *C. psittaci* is well known and is best documented for incidents of human disease, sometimes fatal, acquired from parrots, seabirds, pigeons, turkeys and ducks. Strains of mammalian origin generally are considered to be less virulent for people but some recent instances of sheep-related human infections and illness have drawn attention to the potential human risk. Instances of mild 'flu-like illness among laboratory and vaccine production workers handling ovine strains of *C. psittaci* have been reported and it is conceivable that a similar risk is run by male stock attendants assisting at lambing in known affected flocks. More seriously, several cases of abortion have been recorded in pregnant women, all of whom had close contact with ovine chlamydial abortion. All were very seriously ill.

Appropriate hygienic precautions must be available for flock attendants dealing with abortion problems: at the very least, handwashing facilities and disinfectant should be provided. Pregnant women must be advised to avoid contact with lambing sheep.

CHAPTER 10

Watery Mouth

ANDREW EALES

INTRODUCTION

Watery mouth is not a new problem. It was recognized by shepherds in the 1920s but it is only in the last 20 years, associated with the intensification of lambing, that it has assumed serious and sometimes disastrous proportions.

CLINICAL PICTURE

Watery mouth affects young lambs, usually 12–48 hours old. Initially the lamb appears dull and ceases to suck. Within hours the "watery mouth" appears, saliva drooling over the muzzle. Some lambs show excessive lacrimation. The alternative names "slavery mouth" or "slavers" are perhaps more appropriate. Abomasal tympany is a common finding and in extreme cases is visually obvious, giving the lamb a bloated appearance (Fig. 10.1). If these lambs are "shaken" a splashing sound originating from the abomasum can be heard, the so-called "rattle belly". Untreated cases die within 6–24 hours showing a terminal hypoglycaemia and hypothermia.

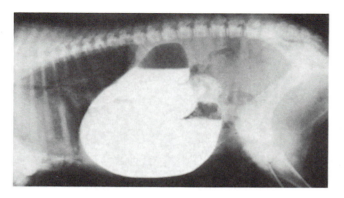

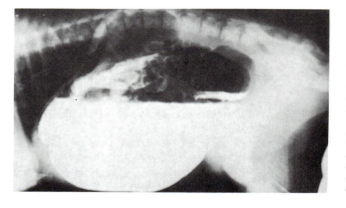

Fig. 10.1
Radiographs taken of lambs after a barium meal. Top: Healthy lamb aged 39 hours. Barium is present in the abomasum (ventral) and the reticulo-rumen (dorsal). The abomasum and reticulo-rumen occupy about one-half of the abdominal cavity. Bottom: Lamb aged 72 hours affected by watery mouth. The abomasum occupies practically the whole abdominal cavity and contains a considerable amount of gas.

SUSCEPTIBLE LAMBS

Susceptibility to watery mouth has been associated with three factors:

(1)   Litter size: Watery mouth is 2–3 times more common in triplets than in singles.
(2)   Ewe body condition: Lambs out of poor ewes are more susceptible.
(3)   Early castration: The early use of rubber rings increases susceptibility.

These three factors, as well as experimental evidence, indicate that the major factor in reducing susceptibility is early and

Fig. 10.2
Early case of watery
mouth. Some saliva
can be seen on the
muzzle. The lamb is
strong — it was
physically restrained
for this photograph.

adequate colostrum intake. A male triplet out of a poor ewe castrated at 1 hour old is unlikely ever to suck colostrum. "Early" means 60 minutes and "adequate" means 50 ml/kg.

DIAGNOSIS

Diagnosis in the early stages of the condition presents few problems. The lamb is usually physically strong, unwilling to suck, its muzzle is covered with thick saliva and its temperature is normal (Figs 10.2 and 10.3). Scouring is unusual.

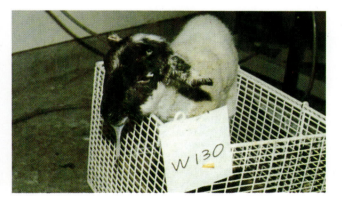

Fig. 10.3
Lamb with watery
mouth showing
excessive salivation.

In the terminal stages or at post-mortem examination, diagnosis is more difficult (Fig. 10.4). Most lambs are hypothermic and salivate when in extremis and the post-mortem picture is that of a lamb which has progressively collapsed and died, often under an infra-red lamp.

RESEARCH FINDINGS

Watery mouth research was piloted at the Moredun Research Institute and this work is still continuing. The major findings are:

(1)   Watery mouth is definitely associated with *Escherichia coli* infection (K99 positive strains have not been found).
(2)   Early colostrum intake is highly effective in preventing watery mouth.
(3)   Gut tone and motility are depressed in watery mouth, the probable cause of the retention of meconium found in some cases.
(4)   Watery mouth is not associated with any prenatal nutritional deficiency.
(5)   Watery mouth is the result of excessive endotoxin production in the gut, derived from dead *E. coli* bacteria.

Fig. 10.4
Weak lamb (no restraint required) showing saliva and milk around the muzzle. Caution should be taken in making a definite diagnosis of watery mouth in this case.

PATHOGENESIS

Work at the Moredun Research Institute by Dr Chris Hodgson
and his colleagues has demonstrated that watery mouth is
primarily an endotoxaemia. This finding has led to a new
name for the condition: "Ovine neonatal endotoxaemia"
(ONE).

At birth the lamb is exposed to a massive oral load of *E.
coli* bacteria. Soiled bedding in the lambing pen is one source
of *E. coli* but another potential source is the ewe herself.
Before lambing the ewe lies in a yard often on badly soiled
wet bedding – this is especially common when silage is fed.
The ewe's belly is thus grossly contaminated (Fig. 10.5). The
newborn lamb's first instinct after standing is to suck and it
finds the teat by trial and error. It sucks anything that it can
take into its mouth and this includes the belly fleece. There
would seem a good chance that the lamb ingests a high
number of bacteria before it finds the teat, i.e. before it has
sucked colostrum (Fig. 10.6).

This indoor situation is in marked contrast to the extensive
outdoor situation where ewe fleece contamination is minimal
and watery mouth is either unusual or unknown.

Ingested *E. coli* will easily pass through the stomach with
its contents at pH 7 (this neutral pH permits immunoglobulins
to reach the small intestine biochemically intact; over the next

Fig. 10.5
Pregnant ewe lying in
a dirty yard. Is this a
source of *E. coli*
infection and watery
mouth for its unborn
lambs?

Fig. 10.6
Newborn lamb
seeking the udder.
Its first "suck" is not
colostrum.

24–48 hours the pH value declines to about 3 as parietal cells develop) to the small intestine.

The exact sequence of events in the small intestine is unclear (a possible sequence is presented in Fig. 10.7) but the result of excessive bacterial multiplication, and thus excessive bacterial death, is the production of endotoxin.

A small amount of endotoxin can be destroyed by the liver, but large amounts will escape into the systemic circulation, and produce a clinical endotoxaemia – watery mouth.

PREVENTION

PROMOTE EARLY COLOSTRUM INGESTION

(1)   Ensure ewes are in good condition (score 3–3.5).
(2)   Do not castrate lambs until 12 hours, and preferably 24 hours, old.
(3)   Manage newborn lambs to maximize early sucking.
(4)   Feed lambs colostrum by stomach tube if they do not suck. Many triplets require this treatment.

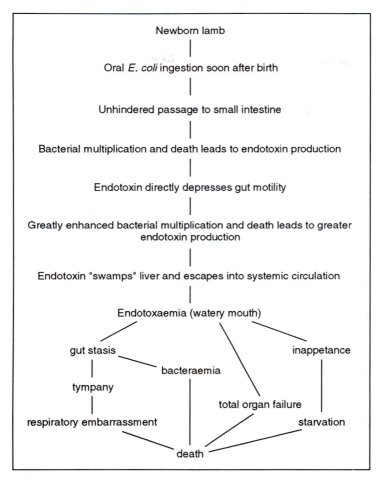

Fig. 10.7 Watery mouth – pathogenesis.

REDUCE EXPOSURE TO INFECTION

(1)   Ensure clean dry bedding throughout the sheep house.
(2)   Clean and disinfect lambing pens between occupants. Do not ignore the yards.

ANTIBIOTICS

If management fails to prevent watery mouth prophylactic antibiotic therapy must be considered. There is very little information available on this subject – I have successfully used oral streptomycin/neomycin and oral amoxycillin but most oral preparations and some injectable ones are in current use. When using antibiotics two points should be borne in mind:

(1)   The earlier the better. The next morning is too late, 15 minutes old seems ideal.
(2)   When using oral preparations ensure the whole dose is swallowed. A black solution dribbling down a black face is very difficult to see.

OTHER DRUGS

If the sequence of events outlined above is near to the truth, one possible line of attack would be to absorb the initial production of endotoxin, and thus avoid any depression of gut motility. A number of agents have been shown to perform this function including kaolin and lactulose.

No mention of watery mouth is complete without a reference to the "Beechams pill", a powerful gut stimulant and purgative. I do not know how effective this agent is but the devotion shown to it by its advocates in the Scottish Borders would suggest that it has some beneficial effect. Such a beneficial effect would support the hypothesis that a depression of gut motility is central to the pathogenesis of watery mouth.

VACCINATION

A few years ago it was suggested that *E. coli* vaccines administered to the ewe before lambing might prevent watery mouth. While some farmers are still using vaccines for this purpose, no evidence has been produced to support their use.

TREATMENT

The treatment of endotoxaemia is notoriously difficult. The present evidence suggests that treatment should achieve three aims:

(1)   prevent starvation;
(2)   depress bacterial activity within the gut until normal tone and motility return; and
(3)   prevent systemic infection.

The following regime has proved effective in 85 % of cases when commenced early in the course of the condition:

(1)   Inject the lamb daily with antibiotic.
(2)   Feed the lamb by stomach tube with 100–200 ml glucose/electrolyte solution containing oral antibiotic three times daily. Use one of the proprietary calf scour mixtures but increase the glucose content to about 10 % (100 g/litre) by the addition of powdered glucose. The feeding of milk is contraindicated.
(3)   Unless the lamb is very sick leave it with the ewe. This will enable it to commence sucking again as it recovers.
(4)   Continue this treatment regime until all signs have gone and the lamb is sucking well from the ewe.

Treatment along these lines is laborious and many sheep farmers would not have adequate labour to treat more than a few lambs thoroughly.

ACTION IN AN OUTBREAK

When faced with an outbreak the following steps are suggested.

(1)   Visit the farm and confirm the diagnosis in early clinical cases – a lamb in extremis brought to the surgery is not adequate evidence on which to make a firm diagnosis.
(2)   Institute treatment for affected lambs.
(3)   Institute prophylactic antibiotic therapy, emphasizing the

importance of timing and dosing technique.

(4)   Note ewe body condition. Score 20 ewes. It will be too late for action this year, but important for the future.

(5)   Note state of yards and lambing pens and advise.

(6)   Question castration policy and advise.

(7)   Question ewe/lamb management immediately after lambing and advise.

(8)   When the situation is stable consider reducing antibiotic prophylaxis. Start with the least susceptible lambs, e.g. singles out of fit mature ewes.

ACKNOWLEDGEMENTS

The author wishes to thank Moredun Research Institute for the radiographs and R. O. Collins for help with the colour slides.

CHAPTER 11

Border Disease

PETER NETTLETON

INTRODUCTION

Border disease (BD) is a congenital disease of sheep first reported from the Border region of England and Wales, and since recorded in sheep-rearing countries throughout the world. The disease also occurs in goats, producing similar signs, but this article will deal solely with BD in sheep.

CAUSE

The cause of BD is a virus serologically related to bovine virus diarrhoea (BVD) virus and swine fever (hog cholera) virus, the three viruses being grouped in the genus *Pestivirus* in the family Togaviridae. Pestiviruses isolated from sheep are termed BD virus (BDV) and those from cattle BVDV, but sheep isolates will infect cattle and vice versa. The natural host range of pestiviruses is restricted to ruminants and pigs.

Serological differences between different isolates of BDV exist. Cross-protection studies with two antigenically distinguishable BD viruses have shown clearly that ewes with immunity to one isolate were susceptible to the other. Nearly all field isolates of BDV are non-cytopathic in cell cultures. There is, as yet, no clear role for cytopathic isolates in the natural history of the disease.

PRESENTING SIGNS

Usually the first evidence of BD in a flock is seen at lambing time. An excessive number of barren ewes, abortions, stillbirths and the birth of small weak lambs may be the only signs (Figs 11.1 and 11.2). Frequently, however, a percentage of lambs will show abnormal body conformation, tremor and hairy fleeces sometimes with abnormal pigmentation; clinical signs which have led to such lambs being described as "hairy shakers" (Fig. 11.3).

Occasionally losses at lambing time are low and veterinary advice is not sought until summer or autumn when a group of lambs is presented in which some have died and others are scouring and/or ill-thriven. The shepherd may or may not recall having a few "hairy shakers" at lambing.

Fig. 11.1
Stillborn lambs infected with BDV. Intra-uterine growth retardation caused by the virus is very variable leading to a wide size range of such lambs.

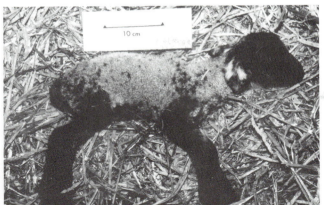

Fig. 11.2
A BDV-infected lamb weighing only 1250 g. This lamb was born alive but was unable to stand and suck.

Fig. 11.3
Three-week-old "hairy shaker" lamb persistently infected with BDV. Hairiness is most prominent along the nape of the neck. Abnormal pigmentation of the fleece may also be a feature in some such lambs.

PATHOGENESIS

INFECTION OF NON-PREGNANT SHEEP

Infection of normal newborn and adult sheep with British isolates and those from many other countries produce only clinically mild or inapparent disease. Viraemia in such animals is short lived and the appearance of neutralizing antibodies approximately 11–14 days after infection coincides with the elimination of the virus.

One French isolate, however, has been shown to produce profound leucopenia and death in 50% of 3- to 5-month-old lambs. Further characterization of this isolate is awaited as it probably contributed to causing "Syndrome X" (also called Aveyron disease or ovine leucopenic enterocolitis), a severe haemorrhagic disease of ewes and lambs.

INFECTION OF PREGNANT EWES

The most serious consequences of BDV infection occur when the virus infects susceptible ewes during pregnancy. The ewes show no clinical signs but virus spreads quickly to the placenta and crosses to the foetus within one week of infection. The immune response of the ewe rapidly eliminates all virus from the maternal tissues but has no effect in the foetus where virus can persist.

"SYNDROME X" OR AVEYRON DISEASE

An unusually pathogenic strain of BD virus was recovered from a case of "Syndrome X", a new disease first reported in December 1983 in the Aveyron region in France among sheep reared intensively for the production of milk used in the manufacture of Roquefort cheese. This new disease, also called Aveyron disease or ovine leucopenic enterocolitis, killed 1500 ewes and 24,000 lambs in 1984. The principal signs were severe depression, pyrexia and diarrhoea, and at post-mortem examination haemorrhages were seen at many sites, being consistently present in the caecum, colon and mesenteric lymph nodes. The incidence of the disease fell sharply in 1985 and although its cause was never determined conclusively, characteristics of the syndrome suggested that it had a viral aetiology. Of the five viral agents recovered, only the BD virus has a strong claim for having made a major contribution to causing "Syndrome X".

FOETAL INFECTION

The ultimate outcome of the foetal infection depends on several factors including the strain and dose of virus, the breed of the foetus and its ability to repair damage. The most important factor, however, is the stage of foetal development at which infection occurs. The age at which the foetus gains immunological competence is critical in determining the distribution and persistence of virus, which in turn influences the extent of foetal damage. The ovine foetus can first respond to an antigenic stimulus between approximately 60 and 85 days of gestation. The possible fates of foetuses infected before or after this crucial period are summarized in Fig. 11.4.

FOETAL INFECTION BEFORE IMMUNE COMPETENCE

In foetuses infected before the onset of immune competence, virus replication is uncontrolled and death of the foetus is likely; death may ensue rapidly leading to resorption or the unnoticed abortion of small foetuses, or may not occur until weeks or months after infection when the subsequent abortion or stillbirths are clearly manifest. It is also possible for one foetus to die in early gestation and be found mummified at the birth of its surviving twin.

In lambs surviving infection in early gestation virus is

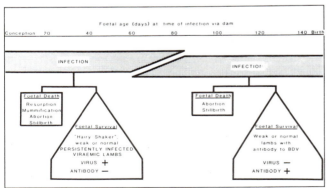

Fig. 11.4
Possible fates of foetuses infected with BDV before or after the development of the foetal immune response between 60 and 85 days of gestation.

widespread in virtually all organs. Typically there is no evidence of any inflammatory reaction. The principal pathological findings are myelin deficiency in the CNS which accounts for the tremor, and an increase in the number of primary hair follicles causing "hairiness". The low pathogenicity of some virus strains, however, means that some lambs can be born persistently infected with virus without showing any clinical signs, and with only minimal pathological lesions. Pre-colostral blood samples from "hairy-shaker" and other persistently infected lambs contain readily detectable amounts of infectious BDV. Such lambs are tolerant to the virus and have a persistent infection usually for life.

FOETAL INFECTION DURING THE DEVELOPMENT OF IMMUNE COMPETENCE

If infection occurs at the time the foetal immune response is developing the outcome is unpredictable; some lambs will be born antibody-positive and virus-negative while others will be viraemic and antibody-negative. Infection at this stage can result also in widespread inflammatory lesions in the CNS leading to cerebral cavitation and cerebellar dysplasia. Lambs thus affected frequently have severe nervous signs and major locomotor disturbances and have high concentrations of serum antibody to BDV.

FOETAL INFECTION AFTER DEVELOPMENT OF IMMUNE COMPETENCE

Infection after 85 days of gestation is met by an immune system capable of destroying the virus. Foetal death is rare and virtually all lambs will be born apparently normal. They will be virus-free but have demonstrable antibody against the virus.

PERSISTENTLY INFECTED LAMBS

Clinically affected lambs have a low chance of survival; many die early in life while survivors have a poor growth rate and an increased susceptibility to other diseases. Less severely affected lambs gradually lose obvious clinical signs of the disease as they mature, and they and apparently normal persistently infected lambs can survive for years.

Most persistently infected lambs will receive colostral antibody to BDV and thus for the first few months of life will be antibody-positive and virus-positive although virus may be recovered only with some difficulty at this stage. However, as these lambs are immunotolerant to BDV they become seronegative as the colostral antibody concentration wanes. Virus persists in most tissues of the affected lambs and they remain a potent source of infectious virus.

Within groups of persistently infected lambs housed apart from all other animals a few aged between 2 and 21 months have developed spontaneously an intractable scour, wasting, excessive ocular and nasal discharges sometimes with respiratory distress. At necropsy such sheep have gross thickening of the distal ileum, caecum and colon resulting from focal hyperplastic enteropathy. Cytopathic BDV can be recovered from the gut of these lambs, and with no obvious outside source of cytopathic virus it is most likely that such virus originates from the lamb's own virus pool. Other persistently infected lambs in the group do not develop the disease. This syndrome, which has also been recognized in occasional field outbreaks of BD, has several similarities with bovine "mucosal disease".

Persistently infected sheep surviving to breeding age often have reduced fertility, but virus-containing semen from a persistently infected ram can produce persistently infected offspring and persistently infected ewes have produced infected lambs in successive pregnancies.

SOURCES OF INFECTION

Sheep-to-sheep contact is the principal way in which BDV is spread, and the most potent source of virus is the persistent excretor. Bought-in persistently infected gimmers have been shown to introduce BDV into a susceptible flock and cause a serious outbreak of BD, and many other outbreaks of BD have a history of introduction of new stock at the beginning of the breeding season. More intensive husbandry, particularly housing during early pregnancy, increases the risk of an explosive outbreak of BD.

Pestiviruses from other species can also under experimental conditions cause BD in sheep so that, among domestic animals, cattle in particular but also goats and possibly pigs represent potential sources of infection. Among free-living ruminants pestiviruses have been isolated from red, roe and fallow deer, and serological surveys in Europe, North America and Africa have shown that many species have detectable antipestivirus antibodies. Therefore, where sheep are grazed extensively in contact with free-living ruminants the possibility of infection from these other species cannot be excluded.

The only other possible source of BDV infection is a live vaccine contaminated with a pestivirus. All vaccines produced in ovine, bovine or porcine cell cultures, or in medium supplemented with serum from these species run the risk of being contaminated with a pestivirus unless meticulous screening techniques are adhered to.

DIAGNOSIS

The diagnosis of BD will present little difficulty to the experienced clinician if typical "hairy shaker" lambs are born. Even so, laboratory confirmation will often be sought because swayback, "daft" lamb disease, bacterial meningoencephalitis, focal symmetrical encephalomalacia and hypothermia may have to be considered in the differential diagnosis.

Placentae and foetuses aborted due to BDV infection have no distinguishing characteristics so, similarly, laboratory confirmation will be necessary to differentiate BD from the other known infectious causes of ovine abortion. The specimens that are required by the laboratory to confirm BD are summarized in Table 11.1.

All the animals in a suspected group should be blood sampled in order to detect the antibody-negative, virus-positive persistently infected sheep, whereas antibody testing of a 10% sample of different age groups of animals can be useful for demonstrating the presence and extent of BDV infection in a flock.

Table 11.1 Specimens to be collected for the laboratory confirmation of BD.

Clinical manifestation	Live animal	Dead animal
"Hairy shaker" or weak lambs Poorly thriving or scouring lambs	Whole blood (clotted or heparinized) for virus isolation and serology from both the lamb and its dam	Thyroid, kidney, brain, spleen, gut and lymph nodes: fresh for antigen detection and in virus transport medium for virus isolation. Heart blood for serology. Brain and spinal cord in calcium formal saline for histopathology
Abortion	Blood from dam for serology and virus isolation	Tissues as above plus placenta for antigen detection and virus isolation. Brain and spinal cord in calcium formal saline for histopathology

CONTROL

Border disease can be controlled only by preventing the exposure of susceptible pregnant ewes to BDV. As the most important source of BDV is the persistent excretor, the identification of such sheep by blood testing will play a crucial role in the control of the disease.

On farms with no history of BD the introduction of replacement breeding stock needs careful consideration. Ideally, replacement females should be home bred, and purchased tups should be tested to ensure they are not persistently infected. Where females are also bought in the feasibility of blood testing them should be considered; newly purchased females should always be tupped and kept separate from the rest of the flock until lambing time.

In a flock which has recently had a sporadic outbreak of BD, the entire lamb crop and the sheep suspected of or shown by blood tests to have introduced infection must be removed from the farm before the start of the next breeding season. Disposal by slaughter is the only way of preventing further spread of disease.

Control of infection in endemically infected flocks by the identification and disposal of persistently infected sheep may not be practicable. In such a flock, control of disease can be achieved by deliberately exposing all breeding stock, at least two months before mating, while they are not pregnant to known persistently infected lambs. Close herding, for at least three weeks and preferably indoors, is necessary for BDV to be spread effectively.

It is very likely that the vaccination of female breeding stock several months before tupping will ultimately play a major role in the control of BD. There is a need to develop a vaccine to protect sheep against both of the antigenically distinguishable strains currently known to cause BD.

FURTHER READING

Barlow, R. M. & Patterson, D. S. P. (1982). *Advances in Veterinary Medicine* **36**, 1–87.

Bonniwell, M. A., Nettleton, P. F., Gardiner, A. C., Barlow, R. M. & Gilmour, J. S. (1987). *Veterinary Record* **120**, 246–249.
Jeffrey, M. & Roeder, P. L. (1987). *Research in Veterinary Science* **43**, 22–27.
Sharp, M. W. & Rawson, B. C. (1986). *Veterinary Record* **119**, 128–130.

CHAPTER 12

Listeriosis in Sheep

CHRIS LOW AND KARL LINKLATER

INTRODUCTION

Listeria monocytogenes infection in sheep is associated with encephalitis, abortion and septicaemia.

In recent years the incidence of both encephalitis and abortions has increased (Fig. 12.1) though the two occur together rarely. Abortions caused by *L. monocytogenes* are most common between December and April and the incidence of encephalitis also shows a marked seasonality with most cases occurring between January and May.

The increasing incidence and seasonality of the disease has been associated with the use of silage as a feed for sheep, though not all outbreaks of listeriosis can be linked with silage feeding.

EPIDEMIOLOGY

L. monocytogenes is ubiquitous and can survive in the environment for years. It has been found in soils, feedstuffs and also in faeces from healthy animals, including human sewage sludge which may be important in the epidemiology of listeriosis.

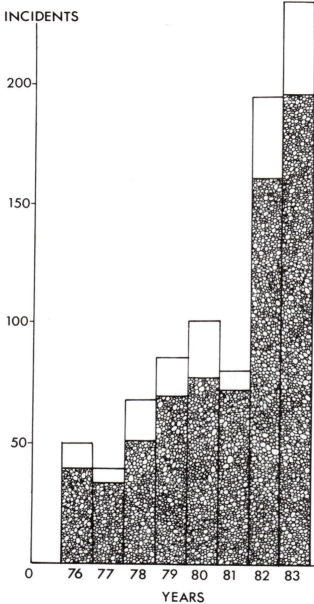

INCIDENTS

YEARS

Fig. 12.1
Annual incidence of
listeriosis 1976–83 in
England, Scotland
and Wales as
collected by the
Central Veterinary
Laboratory,
Weybridge, by the
VIDA II scheme.
Shaded area –
listeriosis other than
foetopathy; white
area – foetal
listeriosis.

Silage becomes a source of infection if soil containing *L. monocytogenes* is included. Poor fermentation of the silage around the areas of soil contamination or where conditions are aerobic will enable the organism to multiply and, after feeding, this may lead to infection. Infection may also arise as a result of soil or faecal contamination of other foods.

L. monocytogenes is a Gram-positive, non-sporing, short bacillus. The organism is easily cultured on 5% sheep blood agar, aerobically at 37°C. After incubation for 24 hours colonies are small with a narrow zone of haemolysis.

Since *L. monocytogenes* is able to multiply at 4°C cold enrichment techniques involving culture for long periods in listeria-selective broth, containing nalidixic acid and thallous acetate at 4°C, aids the isolation from silage and brains, substances from which it is rarely isolated on direct culture.

Serotyping reveals two common serotypes of *L. monocytogenes*, types 1/2 and 4 with type 3 occasionally occurring. Serotype 5 is now known as *L. ivanovii* and is solely associated with abortion in sheep.

CLINICAL SIGNS

Signs of the septicaemia in lambs are dullness, inappetance, pyrexia and diarrhoea. Death may follow in 24 hours. In adults with listerial septicaema a concurrent hypocalcaemia has been found.

Abortions caused by *L. monocytogenes* generally occur late in gestation and there is often a heavy brown vaginal discharge. Death of the ewe may follow as a result of metritis and septicaemia.

A common feature of listerial encephalitis is circling and the first cases described, over 50 years ago, were termed circling disease. Generally there is a unilateral facial paralysis and/or tilting and turning of the head to the same side (Fig. 12.2). Sheep circle or fall to the affected side and often there is an excessive drooling of saliva because of an inability to swallow. Death occurs within a few days and is preceded by recumbency and paddling of the forelimbs. Adults are usually dull but lambs quite often become highly excitable with the

Fig. 12.2
Sheep affected by listerial encephalitis showing typical facial paralysis and head tilting.

onset of clinical signs. The rectal temperature remains normal or may be slightly elevated to 40°C.

POST-MORTEM FEATURES

Gross post-mortem examination of septicaemic cases occasionally reveals focal miliary liver abscesses but lesions are usually few and non-specific.

In cases of abortion gross lesions are a result of intra-uterine autolysis and are non-specific though there may be focal miliary liver abscesses.

No gross lesions are present in cases of listerial encephalitis.

DIAGNOSIS

Diagnosis of listerial septicaemia relies on the isolation of *L. monocytogenes* from visceral organs of carcases or from the blood of live animals. Similarly, the diagnosis of listerial abortion is made after isolating the organism from the foetus. Usually isolation from these cases is not difficult. In listerial encephalitis, however, isolation of the organism is best attempted using the cold enrichment technique on samples of the pons, taken aseptically. Diagnosis must be confirmed by histological examination of the brain.

Examination of the brain may be necessary to differentiate listerial encephalitis from pituitary abscesses and gid but the course of listerial encephalitis is generally days whereas gid is a more protracted illness.

A neutrophilia is found in listerial encephalitis, meningitis and cerebrocortical necrosis but meningitis will be more acute and in cerebrocortical necrosis there is elevation of serum transketolase levels. A leucopenia is found in louping-ill.

Pregnancy toxaemia can be differentiated by the presence of ketone bodies in serum and urine.

PATHOGENESIS

Sheep are probably frequently exposed to infection and other factors influencing susceptibility such as late pregnancy, intercurrent disease and immunosuppression may be important in the development of listeriosis.

Septicaemia is commonest in neonates and lambs and follows 2–3 days after oral infection, though congenital and navel infection can also occur.

Following oral ingestion and penetration of the gut mucosa haematogenous spread leads to infection of the gravid uterus and the presence of *L. monocytogenes* in the placenta, amniotic fluid and foetus within 48 hours. Foetal death occurs as a result of septicaemia possibly following inhalation of amniotic fluid. Extensive oedema and inflammation of the chorioallantois with resultant necrosis leads to abortion. Generally abortion occurs in late gestation, 5–10 days post-infection.

Naturally occurring cases of encephalitis are probably the result of passage of the organism through breaks in the oral mucosa and via branches of the trigeminal nerve to the brain. The incubation period is around 14–32 days and results in characteristic microabscesses unilaterally in the pons in the region of the trigeminal nerve nucleus. The inflammatory response initially consists of microglial macrophages and later neutrophil infiltration and necrosis, together with perivascular cuffing involving lymphoid cells. Occasionally lesions occur in the basal region of the brain with haemorrhage and a purulent leptomeningitis.

It has been suggested that listerial encephalitis is greatest in lambs, 2-year-old and aged sheep, possibly because at these ages teeth are shed or periodontitis is common and the organism is allowed to penetrate the oral mucosa.

TREATMENT

L. monocytogenes shows *in vitro* sensitivity to chloramphenicol, tetracycline, penicillin and treatment of septicaemic cases with antibiotics has given good results. Following abortions antibiotic therapy is indicated to treat any endometritis.

Response to antibiotics is poor once signs of listerial encephalitis have developed, though treatment with oxytetracyclines has occasionally been effective. During outbreaks of listeriosis the prevention of abortion or encephalitis by treatment of the group with antibiotics appears to be of little use.

PREVENTION

To reduce the risk of listeriosis when using silage as a feed for sheep:

(1) Do not use grass from fields with molehills for silage.
(2) Avoid soil contamination of the silage when filling the clamp.
(3) Use additives to artificially lower the silage pH.
(4) Do not feed obviously mouldy areas of silage.
(5) Do not feed silage to sheep if pH exceeds 5, or ash content exceeds 70 g/kg dry matter.
(6) Empty uneaten silage from feed troughs after 24 hours.

ACKNOWLEDGEMENTS

The authors gratefully acknowledge the help of the epidemiology department, Central Veterinary Laboratory, Weybridge, for the figures of incidence as collected on VIDA II, which represents the incidence of listeriosis recorded by veterinary investigation centres in England, Wales and Scotland.

CHAPTER 13

Diagnosis of Pasteurellosis in Sheep

N. J. L. GILMOUR AND J. S. GILMOUR

INTRODUCTION

Although pasteurellosis is perhaps the commonest infectious disease of sheep of all ages, the diagnosis is not always as straightforward as one might expect. In particular, if diagnosis of the very common form – pneumonic pasteurellosis – is based on gross inspection of the lung, mistakes can occur. The epidemiology and signs of pasteurellosis, areas of possible confusion and appropriate diagnostic procedures are presented here.

GENERAL BACKGROUND

Most outbreaks of pasteurellosis of sheep in the United Kingdom are caused by *Pasteurella haemolytica*.

There are two biotypes of *P. haemolytica* (A and T). The biotype classification depends on sugar fermentation reactions: most biotype A strains ferment arabinose whereas T biotype strains do not and all biotype T strains ferment trehalose and A strains do not. The biotypes are further divided by serology. Biotype A comprises serotypes 1, 2, 5, 6, 7, 8, 9, 11, 12, 13, 14 and 16 and biotype T 3, 4, 10 and 15. Untypable strains which correspond in most respects to biotype A also occur.

Strains of biotype A cause pneumonic pasteurellosis in all ages of sheep, although the disease in young lambs is more septicaemic in character. The condition caused by T biotype – systemic pasteurellosis – is an acute disease resulting in sudden deaths in hoggs in the period October to December, although sporadic deaths apparently due to T-type organisms can occur in all ages of sheep throughout the year.

Either biotype of *P. haemolytica* may be carried in the upper respiratory tract and tonsils of a large proportion of healthy sheep and it is presumed that stresses play a part in converting these carriers into clinical cases. The stresses can be infections, e.g. by parainfluenza 3 virus, or less easily defined factors such as "management practices" – dipping, worming and gathering. Warm weather also seems to predispose to pneumonic pasteurellosis. Dietary changes, e.g. introduction to rape or turnips, have been suggested as possible stresses associated with the systemic disease.

PNEUMONIC PASTEURELLOSIS

CLINICAL FINDINGS

A wide variety of clinical signs may occur ranging from sudden death to occasional coughing. The peracute cases are often found dead and this may be the first notice of disease. Sheep or lambs with pneumonia are dull, anorexic, pyrexic and tachypnoeic or dyspnoeic. There may be a mucopurulent oculonasal discharge.

At this stage the diagnosis of pasteurellosis is a tentative one, and it must be emphasized that bacteriological examination of nasal swabs indicates only that *P. haemolytica* is present in the nasopharynx, not that the sheep are affected with pasteurellosis. Confirmation of the diagnosis is only possible after necropsy.

NECROPSY FINDINGS

Gross examination and differential features

At necropsy, pneumonic pasteurellosis presents a variety of appearances, many of which resemble and can be confused with other conditions. Thus further examinations, histological and/or microbiological, should be undertaken as frequently as is practicable, and are essential for confirmation of diagnosis.

Peracute

The lungs of peracute cases (Fig. 13.1) may not exhibit consolidation, but often appear red or purple in colour with frothy fluid exuding from the cut surface. The tracheobronchial linings, too, may be very dark red. A fibrinous pleural/pericardial exudate is usually present. Petechiae and ecchymoses may be found in the subcutis of the neck and thorax, in abdominal organs and under the epicardium.

Acute and subacute

In acute and subacute cases petechiae and ecchymoses as in the peracute cases may be seen and a thick green gelatinous pleurisy and pericarditis may be present. The lungs themselves are reddened and consolidation is usually present, forming dark, firm areas with distribution varying from discrete foci to complete lung involvement. In some cases, irregular areas of lung necrosis are evident, particularly on the cut surface

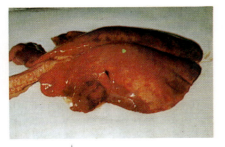

Fig. 13.1
Peracute pasteurellosis. Lungs are reddish/purple, congested and oedematous. *Pasteurella haemolytica* A2 was isolated.

where black or dark green, blood-filled foci are bounded by a greyish margin. Softening and cavitation may be present where necrosis with lysis of tissue has occurred.

Chronic

In chronic cases normal lung tissue is often clearly demarcated from areas of dark red consolidation which may contain pus-filled nodules, and an organizing pleurisy with adhesions is a frequent accompaniment.

Septicaemia in young lambs

In very young lambs, the septicaemic form of pasteurellosis caused by biotype A may give rise only to petechiation of the epicardium, spleen, liver and kidneys accompanied by swelling and hyperaemia of cervical and thoracic lymph nodes. In slightly older lambs (2–3 months), a fibrinous pleurisy with focal lung consolidation may be seen.

Difficulties in differential diagnosis at necropsy

The most reliable diagnostic change at necropsy is the characteristic pattern of necrosis, but there are, as described above, many other forms of pneumonic pasteurellosis. In a peracute case, the lung changes may be confused with other conditions which terminate in acute congestion (Table 13.1), and the situation may be further complicated by hypostatic pneumonia and post-mortem autolysis (Fig. 13.2).

Differing stages of inhalation pneumonia may resemble first, peracute pneumonic pasteurellosis where tracheal froth, congestion, bronchial hyperaemia and pleural exudate are common to both, and secondly, necrotizing pasteurellosis, though the necrotic foci in inhalation pneumonia quickly become suppurative and usually have a wide peripheral distribution.

It should be remembered that pneumonia following dip aspiration and phenolic dip poisoning (Fig. 13.3) both occur in one of the seasonal periods in which pneumonic pasteurellosis is frequently seen.

Table 13.1 Pulmonary conditions resembling pneumonic pasteurellosis at necropsy.

Type of pneumonic pasteurellosis	Conditions which may have a similar lung appearance	Differentiation achieved by
Peracute	Acute congestion – clostridial disease – phenolic dip poisoning	Bacteriology Histology
	Aspiration pneumonia Hypostatic pneumonia } Post-mortem autolysis }	Histology + bacteriology
Acute (necrotizing)	Aspiration pneumonia	Histology + bacteriology
Subacute	Suppurative bronchopneumonia e.g. *Escherichia coli; Actinomyces pyogenes;* *Corynebacterium pseudotuberculosis*	Histology + bacteriology
Chronic	Chronic suppurative bronchopneumonia	Bacteriology
	Atypical pneumonia	Histology
	Chlamydia infection } PI3 infection } Verminous pneumonia }	Histology + bacteriology
	Sheep pulmonary adenomatosis	Histology

PI3 Parainfluenza type 3.

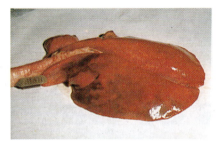

Fig. 13.2
Congestion and autolysis with no evidence of
pulmonary pathogens. The sheep died 12–18 hours
before photograph was taken.

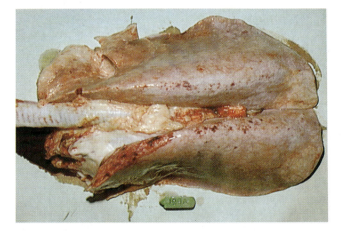

Fig. 13.3
Phenolic sheep-dip
poisoning showing
acute congestion with
visible superficial
haemorrhages.

A gross appearance similar to subacute and chronic pasteurellosis may be produced in pneumonias associated with other
bacteria, e.g. *Escherichia coli* and *Actinomyces pyogenes*, and
pleurisy with abscess formation may also occur in these
infections (Fig. 13.4).

Chronic pasteurellosis in 3- to 12-month-old sheep may be
confused with atypical pneumonia; indeed, *P. haemolytica* A
serotypes are isolated from about 50% of the latter and are
thought to be important, along with *Mycoplasma ovipneumon-
iae*, in its aetiology. The gross lesion in long-standing atypical
pneumonia is a raised area of grey to red consolidation usually
affecting the anterior parts of the lung, compared with the
chronic pasteurellosis lesion which is dark red and depressed,

Fig. 13.4
Pneumonia attributed to *Actinomyces pyogenes*.
There is general congestion, apical consolidation
with pleurisy and abscess formation.

though similarly distributed. A serofibrinous pleurisy resembling that described in pasteurellosis may sometimes accompany atypical pneumonia. Chlamydia, parainfluenza type 3 virus and *Dictyocaulus filaria* may also cause chronic lesions which might require laboratory differentiation from chronic pneumonic pasteurellosis.

Finally, it is worth remembering that at necropsy an apparent pneumonic pasteurellosis may overlie and conceal the grey/pink nodules of sheep pulmonary adenomatosis and it is not uncommon in the UK for acute pneumonic pasteurellosis to be the cause of death in older sheep with primary sheep pulmonary adenomatosis.

Differential histological features

Peracute pneumonic pasteurellosis may have no histological features which might differentiate it from any other condition where pulmonary congestion, haemorrhage and oedema predominate, and the diagnosis then relies upon isolation of large numbers of pasteurella from lung tissue. Poisoning by phenolic sheep dip may be differentiated histologically by its characteristic alveolar epithelialization.

In less acute cases of pneumonic pasteurellosis, characteristic cellular alterations do appear, namely necrosis of alveolar lining cells and clusters of spindle-shaped leucocytes called "oat-cells" occupying alveoli and small airways. Oat-cells have not been described in disease caused by other organisms. If the animal does not die in the very early stages, necrotizing pasteurellosis rapidly evolves into a characteristic histological lesion usually with oat-cells.

Where oat-cells are not present, chronic pneumonic pasteur-ellosis must be differentiated on bacteriological grounds from a non-specific suppurative bronchopneumonia. Atypical pneumonia, however, may be distinguished by its character-istic features of lymphoid nodular hyperplasia, marked hyper-plasia of bronchiolar epithelium, and hyaline scars, which accompany a macrophage and neutrophil exudate. Chlamydia and parainfluenza type virus do not produce a significant neutrophil response, and thus should not be confused histo-logically with chronic pasteurellosis. The prevalence of pneu-monia caused solely by helminths is uncertain but a major contribution by parasites may be assumed when adults or larvae are identified and eosinophils are present in the peribronchiolar cuffs.

Sheep pulmonary adenomatosis lesions, when present, are identifiable by the characteristic adenomatous tumour nodules, which in longer standing cases become confluent. Abroad, it has been recognized that pneumonic pasteurellosis may also complicate a primary maedi lesion. The latter is distinguished by lymphoreticular and smooth muscle hyperplasia, but is not accompanied by a suppurative exudate.

BACTERIOLOGY

Samples for bacteriology, preferably from cases not treated with antibiotics or chemotherapeutic agents, should be taken with instruments which have not been used for the previous stages of the necropsy and which should be heated rapidly by dipping in boiling water between each organ sampled.

Pericardial and pleural fluids can be sampled with swabs. Both tissue and swabs should be transported to the laboratory as quickly as possible and preferably kept refrigerated.

At the laboratory, tissue samples should be treated by a standard method whereby some estimate of the numbers of *P. haemolytica* in the tissues can be obtained. For example, 2–3 g samples of tissue are macerated in 9 ml of nutrient broth and 0.1 ml volumes spread over the surface of a 7% sheep blood agar plate which is incubated overnight at 37°C. Colonies can be counted and the number per gram of tissue calculated.

The number of *P. haemolytica* in the lesions is important since the organisms can be cultured from lungs in the absence of specific lesions but the presence of large numbers of organisms, e.g. 10^6 colony forming units (cfu)/g or more, is a prerequisite for a diagnosis of acute pneumonic pasteurellosis. Smaller numbers (10^3–10^5 cfu/g) are usually isolated from subacute and chronic lung lesions and *P. haemolytica* is often not present in the later lesion of atypical pneumonia.

Bacteriology is essential when suspected breakdown of immunity following vaccination is being investigated. There are 11 different serotypes of *P. haemolytica* biotype A and only the most common of these are present in vaccines. As immunity is serotype-specific it is essential to know what serotype or serotypes are involved. This cannot be ascertained from one necropsy in an outbreak. It is also necessary to confirm pasteurellosis in as many cases as possible and not assume that it was the cause of death in every case. Serotyping is a relatively specialized procedure and is carried out in only a few laboratories.

The measurement of serum antibody titres in experimentally infected sheep has shown that following pneumonic pasteurellosis serum antibody titres do rise. However, this gives only retrospective confirmation of a diagnosis and the number of serotypes involved makes diagnosis by serology a research tool rather than a diagnostic aid at present.

SYSTEMIC PASTEURELLOSIS

CLINICAL FINDINGS

Cases of systemic pasteurellosis are seldom seen alive and there are no pathognomonic signs. Affected sheep are usually very dull or comatose, recumbent, dyspnoeic and frothing at the mouth and, again, confirmation of diagnosis depends on necropsy.

PATHOLOGY

Lesions seen in the respiratory tract at necropsy include congestion, oedema, subpleural haemorrhages, a frothy tracheal exudate and, though much less commonly, focal consolidation. The lesions which characterize the disease, however, include subcutaneous haemorrhages, epithelial necrosis in tongue, pharynx (Fig. 13.5), oesophagus and sometimes abomasum and intestine, enlargement of tonsils and retropharyngeal lymph nodes, and necrotic infarcts in liver and spleen.

Histologically the lung lesions comprise areas of inflammatory cell exudate surrounding bacterial emboli in alveolar capillaries with necrosis and clusters of intensely basophilic organisms. These features should assist in recognizing this lesion and differentiating it from an aspiration pneumonia in particular. However, diagnosis of systemic pasteurellosis at necropsy is more reliably achieved by identifying the characteristic necrotic ulceration in the upper alimentary tract and the focal liver necrosis, another result of lodgement of emboli.

BACTERIOLOGY

The same general principles as for the pneumonic form of the disease apply. Tissues for culture should include lungs, liver and spleen and swabs from alimentary tract ulcers, and again only the recovery of large numbers of organisms is indicative of the presence of the disease. Colonies of T types of *P. haemolytica* are slightly larger and darker than those of the A

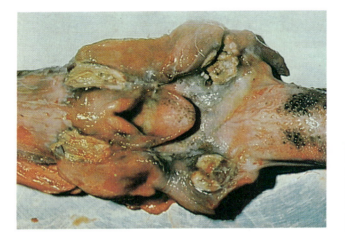

Fig. 13.5
Pharyngeal lesions of systemic pasteurellosis. There are ulcers with necrosis in tonsillar areas and bilateral to larynx.

type. However, further identification depends on serotyping.

Strains untypable by the indirect haemagglutination test are occasionally isolated from sheep which have died of pasteurellosis. Their significance is unknown since it has not been possible to reproduce disease in experimental sheep with these strains, at least by the respiratory route.

DIFFERENTIAL DIAGNOSIS

Any sudden death in one or more of a group of 6- to 9-month-old sheep should be considered as possibly due to systemic pasteurellosis. The pathological features described above would not be found in deaths from clostridial enterotoxaemias. Recovery of *P. haemolytica* type T from the lungs and blood should assist in differential diagnosis and would also be of value in suspected plant poisoning. This group of conditions is too large to describe here. Rumen and abomasal contents should be examined for recognizable leaf fragments, e.g. rhododendron leaves.

CONCLUSIONS

Confirmation of a clinical diagnosis of either form of pasteur-ellosis depends on laboratory examination of specimens taken at necropsy. Sampling should not be confined to just one victim in any outbreak. The gross pathological changes of the disease may be confused with other diseases or obscured by autolysis or hypostatic congestion. Laboratory confirmation depends on the culture of significant numbers of *P. haemolytica* from lesions and/or the presence of specific histological changes.

Serotyping of a number of strains from flock outbreaks is necessary when investigations into the efficacy of vaccination are being made. It cannot be assumed that all deaths are caused by one particular serotype or, indeed, by pasteurellosis.

The recovery of *P. haemolytica* from nasal swabs does not warrant a diagnosis of pasteurellosis and the serotypes present in the nose are not always representative of those causing the disease.

FURTHER READING

Gilmour, N. J. L. (1980). *Veterinary Quarterly* **2**, 191.
Martin, W. B. & Aitken, I. D. (1991). *Diseases of Sheep*. Blackwell Scientific
    Publications, Oxford.

CHAPTER 14

Clinical Aspects of Dental Disease in Sheep

JOHN SPENCE AND GEORGE AITCHISON

INTRODUCTION

Dental disease in sheep should be considered on a flock basis and assessment must be founded upon a sound appreciation of normal dentition and the clinical manifestations, both of specific dental diseases and incidental dental abnormalities.

This article aims to outline those aspects of the ovine dental anatomy of significance to the clinician and to describe how they change in disease. Some of the commoner dental diseases are described.

ANATOMY

TEETH

The sheep has 32 permanent teeth distributed according to the dental formula:

$$2 \left(I\, \frac{0}{3}, \quad C\, \frac{0}{1}, \quad PM\, \frac{3}{3}, \quad M\, \frac{3}{3} \right)$$

where I is incisor, C canine, PM premolar and M molar. The

fourth anterior tooth or canine functionally and morphologically resembles an incisor and will be considered thus for the purpose of this paper.

The permanent incisor tooth tapers from a spade-shaped crown to the root apex with no intervening neck; the deciduous incisors are smaller and have a discernible constricted neck. Between one-third and a half of the fully erupted incisor is visible above the gum margin as the "clinical crown". In a perfect dentition, the incisors are closely aligned with little space between teeth.

All cheek teeth, except the first mandibular premolar, consist of a table, regularly ridged from side to side, and a column of convoluted enamel and dentine surrounded by a thin layer of cementum. Less than one-third of the cheek tooth is visible as the clinical crown. Wear may vary along each row of cheek teeth but changes should be gradual with no steps between teeth.

ERUPTION

All the deciduous teeth erupt within a few days of birth and are functional by 2–4 weeks of age. In contrast, the eruption times of the permanent teeth vary by as much as eight months (Table 14.1). Some of the variation is caused by diet; lowered planes of nutrition delay eruption. The fourth incisor has the

Table 14.1 Eruption times of the permanent dentition.

		Eruption time (months)
Incisors	1	10–19
	2	18–26
	3	23–36
	4	30–48
Premolars	1	18–24
	2	18–24
	3	18–30
Molars	1	3–5
	2	9–12
	3	18–24

Figures give the widest range quoted in four standard ageing references.

most variable eruption pattern and may be totally absent or grossly displaced in up to 5% of all sheep.

PERIODONTIUM (PERIODONTAL LIGAMENT, GINGIVA AND ALVEOLAR BONE)

The incisor teeth are used for gripping and cutting herbage and the support structures making up the periodontium are modified to accept resulting rotating or turning forces met during grazing. These anatomical modifications allow the healthy incisor to move up to 2 mm anteroposteriorly under gentle pressure, but the same features make the sheep incisor very prone to loss following periodontal damage.

On the other hand, the cheek tooth periodontium is designed to hold the tooth in place against the downward and lateral forces of cudding. The length of most cheek teeth and their snug fit within the alveolar bone means that these teeth are lost less often than incisors even when all their ligamentous support has been destroyed.

NORMAL GINGIVA

The pale pink gingiva is closely applied to the teeth to give a thin, evenly scalloped gingival margin. Between the gum and tooth is a shallow groove (gingival sulcus) normally up to 1 mm deep, apart from the lingual aspect of the incisors where it may reach 3 mm. Behind the incisors the gingiva is modified into a keratinized lower denal pad which is used, in conjunction with the upper dental pad, to grip herbage.

GENERAL CLINICAL EXAMINATION

The sheep does not lend itself to a protracted dental examination but useful information can be obtained without recourse to either dental gags or anaesthesia.

Straddling and restraint in a corner of a pen and retraction of the lips allows prolonged access to the animal's incisor region providing that both nostrils are not occluded. Examination of the lingual aspect of the incisors and lower dental pad is possible by further retraction of the lips until the mouth opens.

Clinical examination of the cheek teeth demands the use of a dental gag and torch and then may only be sufficient to show the alignment and angle of the tables and spaces left by missing teeth. Gentle palpation of the ventral and lateral aspects of the mandible through the cheek will detect gaps left by missing teeth, the amount of grass impaction around molars and any localized hard tissue swellings.

A standardized and more detailed dental examination may be required where the long-term dental health of a flock is being monitored. The dental parameters and scoring systems used for this examination, which are similar to those used in man, are listed in Table 14.2.

FEATURES OF CLINICAL SIGNIFICANCE (Tables 14.3 and 14.4)

All sheep show changes in teeth and periodontium which become more pronounced with advancing years. Many appear to have no clinical significance and others may have an importance not yet clearly understood. Any dental examination must distinguish such changes from those which are now recognized as being associated with diseases of economic importance, namely broken mouth, dentigerous cysts, caries, incisor wear, wavy mouth and fluorosis. The following features are affected by one or more of the above syndromes.

TEETH

Tooth status

The presence or absence of incisors, whether they are permanent, deciduous or erupting is important in ageing sheep, though the variation in eruption times limits accuracy. Loss of permanent teeth is still regarded by many flock owners as the only recognizable sign of broken mouth, and they remain unaware of its slow development over a period of 2–3 years.

Table 14.2 Standard clinical examination of sheep incisors for evidence of developing broken mouth. Clinical features and scoring systems used.

Feature (and sites examined)	Score			
	0	1	2	3
Pocket depth (front of central 2 incisors)	0–1 mm Normal	2–5 mm	6–9 mm	10 + mm
Clinical crown height (front of central 2 incisors)	0–6 mm Short	7–12 mm Normal	13–16 mm Normal	16 + mm Long
Tooth movement (central 4 incisors)	Slight movement Arc <5°	Resistance to movement with sharp "stop" at each end of travel. Returns to central position. Arc 5–15°	No resistance to movement and no sharp "stop" at end of travel. Remains out of alignment. Arc >15°	
Recent recession (front of 4 central incisors)	No evidence of recession. Surface deposits down to gingival margin	Pale crescent between gingival margin and tooth surface deposits ≤1 mm	Pale crescent between gingival margin and tooth surface deposits >1 mm	
Gingivitis (front of 4 central incisors)	Gums pale and flat or pale and fibrotic from previous insults — Normal	Mild, localized gingivitis. Local redness of gingiva close to tooth. Little or no oedema	Gingivitis distributed more widely around each tooth and more evident. Gingival oedema also present. On occasion oedema present alone	Gums fiery red and oedematous. May be pus in sulcus. Gums bleed easily. Localized necrosis/trauma possible
Occlusion or bite of whole incisor row	Teeth meet upper pad >5 mm from front edge	Teeth meet on pad within 5 mm of front edge. Normal	Incisor cutting edge rests forward of the front edge of the pad. Teeth may not be in contact with pad	

Table 14.3 Important dental diseases of sheep.

Name	Common presenting signs	Other clinical signs	Aetiology/pathogenesis	Treatment/prophylaxis
Dental caries	Loss of crowns of deciduous teeth in 8- to 12-month-old lambs. Irregular crowns	Preceded by holes in enamel at gum margin	Unknown. Associated with high "sugar" diets	No treatment. Reduce time on root crops, replace with brassicas
Excess incisor wear	Incisor crowns worn flat or below dental pad. Smooth "pearls"	None	Unclear. Soil content of pasture, intensity of grazing, enamel softness	No treatment
Cheek tooth wear	Ill-thrift in a few ewes and dribbling during cudding	Irregular wear of cheek teeth, overgrowth of opposite teeth	May be associated with periodontal diseases or abnormalities of wear	Rasping–only short term
Fluorosis	Excessively worn pair of incisors	Chalky worn bands around teeth	High levels of fluorine during tooth development	No treatment. Prevent access to fluoride

Periodontal disease **Acute** Takes a number of forms, e.g. acute necrotic ulcerating gingivitis	Acute gingivitis, local necrosis around incisors. Any age of animal affected	Cheek teeth region may be involved without incisor region being affected. Halitosis	Bacterially induced. Little known about specific aetiology	No treatment. Changing management to limit excess forces on incisors may extend life of teeth. Dental splints extend tooth life
Chronic, e.g. broken mouth	Incisor looseness and loss, usually with lengthening and proclination. Commonest in older age groups	Intermittent bouts of gingivitis 2–3 years before tooth loss. Pocketing. Cheek teeth periodontium also involved where may have periostitis as a complication	Bacterially induced periodontal disease but with important environmental component	
Dentigerous cysts	Swollen anterior jaw – may be unilateral	Swelling involves incisor region, one or more teeth missing, rest malpositioned	Unknown. Abscessation during tooth development suggested	No treatment

Table 14.4 Definitions of terms used in clinical descriptions of sheep's teeth.

Apically	Descriptive term: towards the deepest portion of the root
Brachygnathia	Lower jaw short relative to upper jaw
Calculus	Mineralized deposit on the tooth surface. Synonymous with "tartar"
Coronally	Descriptive term: towards the cutting/grinding surface of the crown
Gingival margin	This is the line of gingival tissue closest to the tooth crown
Gingival sulcus	Shallow groove between the tooth and the most coronal part of the gingival margin lined with sulcal epithelium
Gum recession	Apical (i.e. towards the root) movement of the gum margin
Maleruption	Abnormality in the tooth eruption process, e.g. outside the normal age range
Malposition	Deviation of tooth from vertical axis or rotation of tooth on long axis or eruption outside arcade
Passive eruption	The movement of the tooth up out of the gums after normal eruption is complete. Results from the lack of opposing cheek tooth or dental pad
Periodontal	Pertaining to tissues which support the tooth. Synonymous with paradontal, periodontal preferred
Periodontal ligament	Dense connective tissue enveloping the roots of teeth, located between cementum and alveolar bone and extending coronally to the alveolar crest
Pocket	Abnormal deepening of the gingival sulcus
Proclination	Forward angulation of the incisors
Prognathia	Lower jaw long relative to the upper jaw
Retroclination	Backward angulation of the incisors
Sulcus	See gingival sulcus

Fig. 14.1
Four-year-old ewe with "perfect" incisor dentition. Note even, scalloped gingival margin and spade-shaped teeth.

Incisor tooth shape

The shape of the incisor tooth can change markedly with age. Perfectly healthy aged ewes should have closely packed, short, spade-shaped incisors (Fig. 14.1.) However, peg-like teeth (Fig. 14.2) are very common in flocks where dental disease is not a problem and probably arise as a result of natural tooth-to-tooth wear and passive incisor eruption. However, long peg-like teeth commonly occur as a result of damage to the

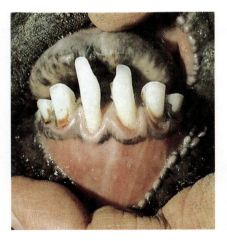

Fig. 14.2
Five-year-old ewe showing long peg-like central incisors with V-shaped mesial wear. Gingiva oedematous and reddened. Second incisors show pale crescents above the gingival margin, evidence of gum recession.

periodontal ligament in developing broken mouth and in association with congenital errors of occlusion or bite, and a check should be made for these conditions where such teeth are seen.

Abrasion to the tooth during grazing and cudding can wear the tooth down to the level of the lower dental pad (Fig. 14.3). In many parts of the world, for example the USA, Ireland and New Zealand, excess wear is a flock problem which can reduce incisors to pebble-like structures in 1–2 years, thereby severely reducing grazing efficiency. In the UK excess incisor wear is uncommon and has never been recorded as a flock problem.

Grooves close to the gum margin may occur following grazing of tough pastures and must be differentiated from caries and acid etching. Lateral or mesial crown wear giving V-shaped notches (Fig. 14.4) between teeth appears to be associated with tooth-to-tooth contact, local trauma during eruption or may occur as a consequence of normal incisor movement. These types of wear will be exacerbated where tooth supports are damaged (as in broken mouth) but alone are not pathognomonic of dental disease and have little deleterious effect upon feeding.

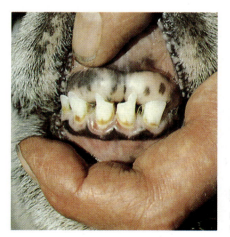

Fig. 14.3
Three-year-old ewe showing wear on central incisor crowns. The rear of the crowns is worn flat leaving a thin lip on the buccal aspect of the crown.

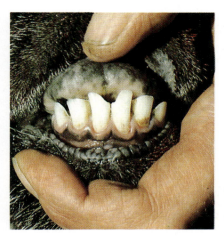

Fig. 14.4
Three-year-old ewe whose central incisors have V-shaped notches. Severe gingivitis (grade 2) evident below central incisors.

Irregular cheek tooth wear

Irregular wearing of the cheek teeth occurs sporadically as a flock problem in the UK, particularly in parts of the Midlands and eastern counties of England. The first signs of the condition may be an increasing incidence of pregnancy toxaemia since pregnant ewes with molar problems are unable to achieve an adequate food intake. Otherwise there is slow deterioration in condition of a few ewes who dribble during cudding and have severe halitosis due to grass impaction. Digestive upsets may follow as a consequence of incomplete food mastication. A definitive diagnosis can only be made following a full dental examination of the cheek teeth.

Irregular wear shows as "steps" between cheek teeth and may result from cheek tooth loss, tooth loosening or maleruption. The opposing teeth passively erupt into the gap left by the missing or moved tooth, abrading the mucous membrane of the cheek and the surrounding gums.

Abnormal molar wear is often seen in association with developing broken mouth and may occur as a result of the damage to tooth supports. Other factors may be important in the development of cheek tooth wear but further research is required before the relationships between wear, local inflammatory gum disease and dental anatomy are properly appreciated.

Wavy or shear mouth is recognized by abnormal angulation

and peaking of the tables, exceedingly sharp cutting edges and, subsequently, damage to surrounding soft tissues. Such abnormal wear tends to occur in only a few animals within the flock and may be caused by abnormalities in cudding movements or the structure of mandible and/or temporo-mandibular joint.

Tooth quality

Teeth enamel is normally a polished "translucent white" but occasionally one or more pairs of permanent teeth have an overall chalky irregular surface which wears very rapidly, or a soft chalky band round the crown. The ingestion of high levels of fluorine during tooth development, for example, following the pasture application of fluorine-rich phosphate fertilizers, has been implicated. The final clinical picture depends upon amount ingested and duration of uptake.

Enamel pitting, localized hypo-amelogenesis, is an incidental finding during dental examination. Pinhead-sized pits may be spread diffusely over the crown or as a band around the tooth. They are more discrete than the lesions seen in fluorosis and occur without softening of the enamel. Though the reasons for this lesion remain unclear, it is probable that a number of systemic metabolic insults occurring during ameloblast activity or trauma to the tooth bud may induce pitting. For example, protein malnutrition following severe intestinal parasitism of lambs.

Deep circumscribed holes close to the gum margin are evidence of caries or acid etching. While occasionally seen around permanent teeth they are more common around deciduous teeth and are most regularly seen in overwintering lambs. The erosions weaken the crowns so much that they snap off leaving irregular stumps (Fig. 14.5). Affected animals have trouble feeding on whole root crops and may lose condition. Age and an irregular tooth stump differentiate these teeth from severely worn incisors. It is postulated that the cause of caries in sheep is similar to that in children, with sugar/soluble carbohydrate levels in the diet playing a significant role.

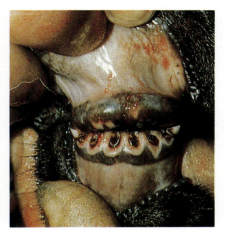

Fig. 14.5
One-year-old gimmer showing the results of caries.
Six central incisors present only as irregular
stumps, fourth incisors normal.

TOOTH SURFACE DEPOSITS

Supragingival bacterial plaque (bacteria attached to the tooth above the gingival margin) is found on all teeth at the entrance to the gingival sulcus. The bacterial plaque may play a role in the development of caries but is unlikely to be associated with periodontal disease and broken mouth. Supragingival plaque should be differentiated from the hidden, complex bacterial flora found in the tooth sulcus (subgingival plaque) which is of prime importance in the initiation and development of gingivitis, periodontitis and tooth loss.

Brown staining of the teeth is common and very variable (Fig. 14.6). It is caused by food staining the porous cementum that covers the enamel and is lost as the cementum is worn away during grazing. Thicker mineralized deposits, or calculus, commonly build up on cheek teeth and, less often, on incisors. The amount, colour and consistency vary enormously from flaky coal-black deposits to mirror-like, hard metallic silver or bronze incrustations. The significance and cause of this variation remains unclear. Where large amounts of material collect, local damage to the gingiva and sulcal entrance may result, influencing the development of local periodontal disease.

Food impaction between and around the teeth of sheep is common, particularly where cheek teeth have been lost and incisors are peg-like and long. The most common site of

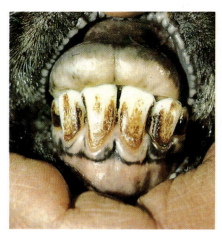

Fig. 14.6
Three-year-old ewe with brown staining of incisors.
Note distribution towards base and between
crowns. Evidence of slight gingivitis (grade 1)
around central incisors.

impaction along the cheek arcade is between the third premolar
and first molar and appears to be associated with the different
ages at which these two teeth erupt. A recent investigation
suggests that grass impaction around incisors may be commoner on farms where broken mouth occurs and that it may
exacerbate local gingivitis and periodontitis. Removal of the
impacted material from around the sheep's incisor often
exposes an acute gingivitis with raw, bleeding, smelly gums.

OCCLUSION

Until recently the terminology applied to occlusion or bite in
sheep has been inconsistent and confusing. Standardized
terms for many of the dental conditions of sheep are now
available.

In animals with normal dentition, the incisors meet the
upper dental pad within 5 mm of its anterior edge, the position
depending upon the relative lengths of the mandible and
maxilla, the angles of the anterior incisors within their sockets
and the length of the clinical crown. All three change with
age, incisors drifting forward on the upper dental pad with
age.

The commonest clinical abnormality of bite which reduces
grazing ability is the malpositioning of the incisors on the
front of the dental pad. While severe congenital prognathism

does occur, this type of bite is most often caused by the abnormal proclination of incisors. Teeth meeting far back on the pad are less common and are more likely to be a result of congenital brachygnathia rather than retroclination.

Recent research suggests that proclination, and resulting malpositioned incisors, most often results from periodontal disease and is neither a highly heritable trait nor a prime cause of broken mouth, as suggested in the past. The present importance placed on subtle differences in the "bite" of ram lambs is thus misplaced unless prognathia or brachygnathia is severe.

GUMS OR GINGIVAE

Gingivitis

Inflammation of the gums may be found in almost all sheep but normally remains slight and localized. The only visible sign of slight gingivitis is a localized redness of the gingival margin close to one or more teeth.

Severe gingivitis, with reddening, swelling and oedema of the gingival margin, occurs in those flocks which develop broken mouth and may appear up to 2–3 years before teeth are actually lost (Figs 14.7 and 14.8). Periodontitis involving the deeper tissues and alveolar bone follows upon gingivitis

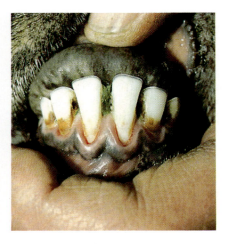

Fig. 14.7
Three-year-old ewe with severe gingivitis of the gingiva below the four central incisors (grade 3). Gums are fiery red and oedematous. Slight food impaction evident between central incisors.

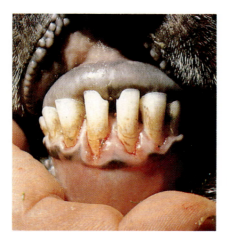

Fig. 14.8
Three-year-old ewe showing severe gingivitis (grade 3), bleeding gums and traumatic damage close to the tooth with misshaped gingival margin as a result. Mesial wear evident centrally.

but can only be diagnosed with certainty by histology. However, its presence may be deduced from the occurrence of gingival pockets.

In animals developing broken mouth the severity of clinical gingivitis fluctuates with time. Seasonal changes in management, diet and weather influence the severity of gingivitis but the significance of these observations and the complex interactions between subgingival plaque, host, management, diet and the rate of development of broken mouth have yet to be unravelled despite intensive epidemiological studies.

A severe gingivitis is often apparent around erupting incisors and cheek teeth. This plays little or no role in the development of periodontal disease and usually regresses within weeks of eruption.

Frank gingival necrosis close to the teeth, with associated severe gingivitis, bleeding and periodontitis, occurs in acute necrotic ulcerative gingivitis, a specific syndrome. This occurs as a flock problem in parts of New Zealand but has been recognized, to date, only in a few animals in the UK.

Traumatic damage

Damage to the gums and either the upper or lower dental pad is common and is associated with the sheep's grazing habits. Commonest sites affected are the gums and the gingival margin below the two central pairs of incisors. Abrasions at either site often ulcerate but heal without treatment within days, leaving little scarring unless close to the tooth, where-upon gum recession and misshaped gingival margins result. It is likely that such trauma will speed the development of broken mouth but this has not been proved.

Gingival pocket

A gingival pocket is a deepening of the gingival sulcus following damage to the tooth supports. In broken mouth pocketing occurs around the incisors in the year before tooth loss, i.e. long after gingivitis is first evident. In the same animals pockets are also found around many of the cheek teeth.

Incisor pockets may be examined by gently dropping a "periodontal pocket probe" down the sulcus parallel to the tooth (Fig. 14.9). The probe will penetrate to the bottom of the pocket with little trouble except on the lingual aspect of the incisors where the curvature of the tooth traps the probe. In advanced periodontal disease pockets may reach up to 1 cm deep around the incisors and may extend to 3 cm or more round the molars.

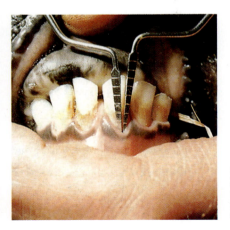

Fig. 14.9
Four-year-old ewe. A periodontal pocket probe is inserted into a 4 mm deep pocket with a second probe being used to demonstrate the pocket depth. Grade 2 gingivitis also evident.

Gingival recession

Gingival recession is the relative movement of the incisor upwards out of the gum or the downward contraction of the gingiva following periodontal tissue damage. It is recognized clinically by the presence of pale crescents of newly exposed cementum close to the gingival margin. The size of these crescents fluctuate with time in a similar way to gingivitis and often increase following bouts of severe gingivitis.

BONE

Bony swellings of the anterior mandible

Localized, unilateral bony swellings of the mandible below the incisors may occasionally become a flock problem, the associated incisor displacement preventing 2- to 4-year-old animals from grazing normally. Flock outbreaks have been reported in the UK and New Zealand.

Radiography will reveal a swelling which is cystic in nature and situated within the alveolar bone, one or more incisors being embedded in its wall (Fig. 14.10). The pathogenesis of the condition is unknown but it is suggested that the swellings arise as a result of periodontal abscesses around developing incisors. The sporadic nature and flock incidence of the condition suggests that environmental features may play a significant role.

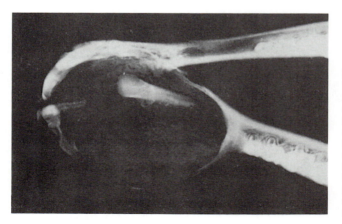

Fig. 14.10
Radiograph of a mandible from a 3- to 4-year-old ewe with anterior mandible swelling. Note the cystic nature of the swelling, the displaced erupted incisors and the single buried incisor associated with the cyst wall.

Bony swellings of the posterior mandible

Bony swellings around cheek teeth, which can be palpated from the lateral and ventral aspects of the jaw, are occasional findings in many flocks. However, in those areas where cheek tooth wear problems are common their prevalence increases. The swellings are caused by a localized periostitis and subsequent organization. The associations between periostitis, cheek tooth wear and tooth loss suggest that this lesion is a complication of acute or chronic periodontal disease of the cheek teeth. The commonest site affected is between the third premolar and first molar tooth, the site where grass impaction most often occurs.

TREATMENT

At present there is no way of treating dental diseases of sheep on a flock basis. All suggestions made to the farmer must be extremely empirical and applicable to individual animals. Theoretical approaches to treatment fall into three categories: drug therapy, dental treatments and management changes (Table 14.5).

DRUG THERAPY

ANTIMICROBIAL AGENTS

Broad spectrum antimicrobial agents have been used in the treatment of gingivitis in man and a role may be suggested

Table 14.5 Approaches to treatment of dental disease in sheep.

Drug	(1)	Antimicrobial agents
	(2)	Vaccines
Dental treatments	(1)	Dental splits or prostheses
	(2)	Rasping and crown clipping
	(3)	Dental "surgery"
Management changes		

for them in sheep. However, the few trials completed to date give conflicting results. A single large dose of oxytetracycline is claimed to have improved the dental health of a single flock severely affected with acute molar gingivitis and periostitis. On the other hand, an attempt to influence the development of broken mouth by long-term treatments with two broad-acting antimicrobial agents, including oxytetracycline, has proved ineffective.

Vaccines

While bacteria are implicated in the pathogenesis of broken mouth no single species has been or is likely to be implicated. Vaccine development can only follow studies of the complex bacterial flora in the subgingival plaque and the associated ovine immunological responses. These studies are only in their early stages though they have shown that the subgingival flora has many similarities to that found associated with periodontal disease in other species (including man).

DENTAL TREATMENT

Dental splints

A prosthetic appliance designed to extend the useful life of incisor teeth of sheep has been on the market for a number of years. A stainless-steel bar, shaped to fit round all the incisors of a 3- to 4-year-old ewe, is fixed in position with a quick-setting dental cement (Fig. 14.11). This produces "one tooth with eight roots" which protects the already damaged periodontium from further damage by distributing grazing forces evenly between all incisors. The present policy of the splinting company is to fit the splint in the year before culling with the aim of getting a further year's production from the ewe.

Early models of the dental splint were soon lost but later types have a survival rate of over 90% 18 months after insertion, though most are lost in the 6 months thereafter. There are marked limitations in their use because they can only be fitted to certain types of dentition. For example, teeth

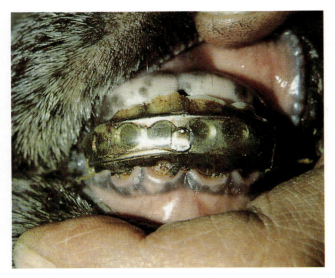

Fig. 14.11
Four-year-old ewe
with a dental splint
around its incisors.
The steel strip is
clear within the
dental cement. This
example has been in
place for 15 months.
Note the continuing
presence of
gingivitis.

must be long enough to accept the splint and binding cement
but teeth must not be loose. Many questions about splinting
and splinted animals remain to be answered. The influence
of splinting on ewe productivity, the best time for fitting and
the type of flock most likely to benefit from their application
have not been clearly determined. Present experience and the
few investigations reported all suggest that the splint is, at
best, a temporary treatment resulting in little flock production
benefit.

Rasping and clipping

Rasping has been successfully used in the treatment of wavy
and shear mouth in individual ewes but the response is short
lived since, in common with all dental treatments, only the
effects are treated, not the cause.

Various clipping and rasping techniques carried out on a
flock basis (ranging from simple pliers to "sanding" with
motor-driven sanding disks) have been advocated for the
control of broken mouth by shortening the crown and returning
the bite to something akin to normal. However, not only do
the limitations mentioned above apply but considerations of

animal welfare also arise. Removing a portion of the incisor crown may expose the pulp cavity, causing pain and predisposing to apical tooth abscesses. Furthermore, the speed of the mechanized operation may splinter the crown allowing bacteria to enter the pulp cavity and periodontium. Although clipping and rasping are commonly practised in Australia there is no scientific evidence to suggest that they are of benefit. All trials carried out to date suggest that no production benefit results from grinding procedures and tooth life is extended by no more than a month or two. Due to the welfare implications all procedures to correct bite using mechanical grinding techniques have been banned in the UK.

Dental surgery

While such conditions as periapical and gingival abscesses may improve following surgery, such treatments are not economical propositions for the flock owner and, as such, should not normally be considered.

MANAGEMENT CHANGES

All the work carried out to date suggests that the interactions between management and broken mouth are complex and almost unique to each flock examined and no general advice on control is possible. Proposals have recently been made as to feeding regimes of lambs and hoggs in flocks prone to broken mouth but these recommendations do not stand up to scientific scrutiny and should not be considered as a general preventative measure. It should be remembered that any change in management will not be reflected in the broken mouth status of the flock until up to four years later.

However, the losses incurred by flock owners have induced a radical change in the management of some hill/upland flocks that may have more general application. When broken mouthed ewes, that would otherwise have been culled, have been retained and maintained for a further year under better conditions than their compatriots, the flock owners report a net financial gain since the resulting reduced replacement costs outweigh their increased feeding costs. Farmers who have access to improved pasture or supplementary feeding may consider retaining their older ewes since cosseted animals produce a further lamb crop with minimum of trouble. Where cheek teeth are involved this approach is unlikely to work because of the inability to ruminate efficiently.

FURTHER READING

McCourtie, J., Poxton, I. R., Brown, R., Whittaker, C. R., Spence, J. A. & Aitchison, G. U. (1990). *Journal of Medical Microbiology* **31**, 275–283.

Page, R. C. & Schroeder, H. E. (1982). *Periodontal Disease in Man and Other Animals. A Comparative Review.* S. Karger, Basel.

Spence, J. A. (1983). In *Diseases of Sheep* (ed. W. B. Martin). Blackwell Scientific Publications, Oxford.

CHAPTER 15

Controlling Tick-Borne Diseases of Sheep in Britain

HUGH REID

INTRODUCTION

Ticks and the diseases associated with them are a major concern of shepherds raising sheep on rough grazings through-out Britain. However, as the severity of the problem varies markedly over quite small areas the appropriate control strategy for each farm has to be individually considered but, invariably, relies on appreciation of the biology of the sheep tick (*Ixodes ricinus*).

LIFE CYCLE

Ixodes ricinus is a three-host tick and its life cycle from egg to adult takes three years (Fig. 15.1). All stages quest by climbing to the tips of the vegetation and waiting for a suitable host to brush against them. As they do not normally walk laterally but only move up and down the vegetation their spread relies entirely on transport by animals. Once attached to a host, immature stages feed for 3–5 days, then drop back into the vegetation where they digest their blood meal, moult and seek a new host only after approximately 12 months.

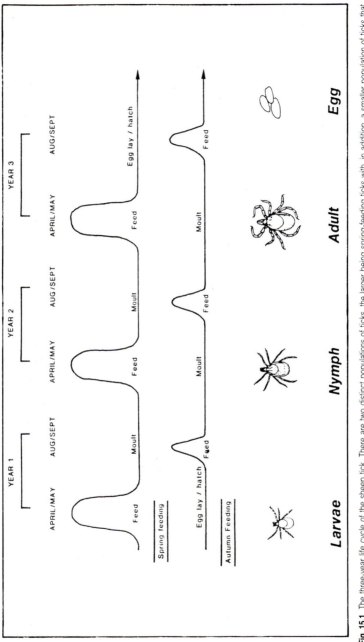

Fig. 15.1 The three-year life cycle of the sheep tick. There are two distinct populations of ticks, the larger being spring-feeding ticks with, in addition, a smaller population of ticks that feed in the autumn in the west of the country.

Adult females complete their blood meal over 14 days, during which time copulation occurs, and then return to the soil where they lay their eggs during the next one or two months. Each female lays 1000–2000 eggs which hatch during the summer. The emerging larvae do not feed until the following year. While the immature stages feed on any vertebrates that live in the same habitat, the adult stages will only feed on large mammals such as sheep, cattle or hares. Thus, with few exceptions, adult ticks rely on sheep for their blood meals. It is the availability of sheep that determines the abundance of ticks in most habitats.

Generally, ticks begin to quest during April when temperatures rise above a critical threshold of 7°C. During the succeeding eight weeks there is a marked peak of activity, followed by a rapid decline, as ticks either attach to a host or desiccate and die. Ticks that fail to feed in spring will not survive through the summer months.

In some western parts of the country there is an additional autumn rise of ticks representing a separate population which overwinters as fed ticks, digest blood meals and moult during the following summer.

Thus during the three-year life cycle ticks are parasitic for only about three weeks, the rest of the time being spent in the vegetation where they require a very humid atmosphere. This microclimate is generally available throughout the rough pastures of the British Isles, particularly on the western seaboard. However, where drainage and land improvements have taken place the soil may dry during the summer months and ticks cannot survive, resulting in a decrease or elimination of the tick population.

CONTROL OF TICK-BORNE DISEASES

Apart from the direct effects of tick parasitism, louping ill and tick-borne fever are two diseases of sheep specifically associated with ticks. Tick-borne diseases can be controlled by either reducing contact with the tick, or by specific prophylaxis for the disease. In deciding the appropriate level of control to attempt in a sheep flock, the effect of ticks on other enterprises on the farm such as cattle rearing and sporting interests should be considered as these may also benefit indirectly from the control policy.

TICK CONTROL

Long-term reduction of tick numbers may be achieved through drainage and re-seeding, but such programmes are seldom embarked upon primarily to achieve control of ticks. Grazing strategies in which the infected pasture is destocked at the beginning of the tick active period, followed some weeks later by exposure of animals recently treated with appropriate anti-tick insecticides, can have dramatic effects on tick numbers if continued over a number of years. However, such treatment alone is generally ineffective as the essential frequent re-application of insecticides is not feasible throughout the tick season on most extensive rough pastures.

Preparations such as dieldrin with extremely long half-lives are no longer acceptable environmentally, but the new generation of synthetic pyrethroid pour-on preparations appear to combine persistence on the fleece without residual toxicity in the carcase or the environment. Their ease of application, safety for young lambs and persistent activity suggest that these agents could provide a high degree of control and, if systematically applied over a period of years, could result in a very marked reduction in parasitism.

CONTROL OF LOUPING ILL

Louping ill is an acute virus disease of the central nervous system which affects all categories of domestic livestock but is particularly associated with sheep.

Following infection, sheep develop a viraemia for a few days when they can infect other ticks but generally are not clinically ill. However, at this time virus invades the central nervous system and a proportion of sheep either die rapidly or develop clinical disease which is characterized by incoordination, ataxia and paralysis, followed by coma and death

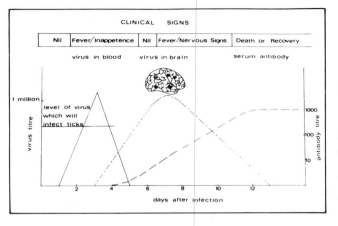

Fig. 15.2
Principal features of louping ill virus infection of the sheep. Note high titres (scale $\log_{10}$) of viraemia required to infect the tick and absence of blood-borne virus during the encephalitic phase of the disease.

(Fig. 15.2). All animals which recover remain antibody positive and immune to infection for life. Diagnosis on clinical grounds is difficult and recourse to laboratory tests will usually be required (Figs 15.3–15.6). A presumptive diagnosis may be made by detection of typical histological lesions, but specific diagnosis relies on virus isolation and/or detection of specific antibody.

All ages of sheep may be affected and, depending on the intensity of challenge, disease can be seen in different

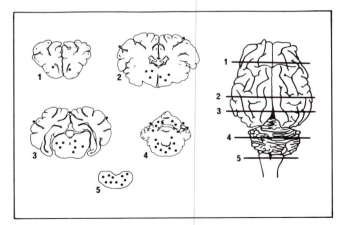

Fig. 15.3
Characteristic distribution of neuropathological changes in brain of sheep with louping ill. (Courtesy of Dr D. Buxton)

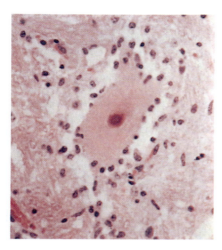

Fig. 15.4
Louping ill virus multiplies in the cytoplasm of
neurones in the brain resulting in necrosis. Note the
small, dark, degenerate nuclei and the
characteristic pink cytoplasm with loss of Nissl
granules. Another characteristic of the disease is
neuronphagia–a clustering of glial cells around the
affected neurone. Haematoxylin and eosin.

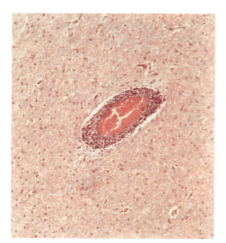

Fig. 15.5
Louping ill virus infection. Section of brain showing
the characteristic cuffing of a blood vessel by
lymphocytes. Haematoxylin and eosin.

categories of animals. Typically, however, when there is a
high prevalence of virus, lambs are protected in their first
year of life by antibody acquired in the colostrum. Replacement
breeding stock are vulnerable to infection at one year old and
it is this category of animal that experiences heaviest losses.
Most surviving animals will have been infected during this
second year of exposure and are subsequently immune.

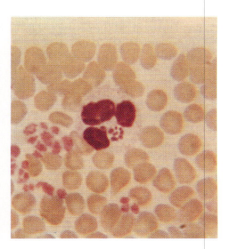

Fig. 15.6
Rickettsial parasites of tick-borne fever multiply primarily in neutrophils and in Giemsa-stained blood smears appear as clusters in cytoplasmic vacuoles. (Courtesy of Dr G. Scott)

Control is by vaccination which should be applied initially to all stock and, subsequently, to all replacement animals and those being introduced to the farm at least one month before exposure to infection. As louping ill is thought to be maintained in a tick/sheep cycle, systematic vaccination over a period of years may eliminate the virus. However, if ticks remain prevalent on the farm, virus can be re-introduced and cause explosive outbreaks if vaccination has been discontinued for a number of years.

Louping ill virus is extremely pathogenic to red grouse and control from this aspect must also be considered if they play a significant economic role on an estate. Red grouse can also amplify the prevalence of virus infection in ticks.

TICK-BORNE FEVER

Infection by the agent of tick-borne fever, a Rickettsial parasite known as *Cytoecetes phagocytophila*, is generally benign but can predispose to other diseases, in particular tick pyaemia, abortion and metritis. Unlike louping ill virus, which normally infects fewer than 1:1000 ticks, the tick-borne fever agent is an extremely efficient parasite and infects most ticks. Hence infection can be transmitted by very small numbers of ticks. The duration of immunity following infection is variable and may last for as little as a few months or extend for more than a year but resistance is generally maintained between periods of tick activity. Strain variation does exist and while animals which recover are likely to be immune to infection by all strains on one farm, they may still be susceptible to infection by strains from a different area. Unlike louping ill no protection is provided by colostral antibody and lambs can become infected as soon as they are exposed to ticks.

Uncomplicated infections are accompanied by high fever (more than 40°C) partial inappetence and listlessness but these clinical signs are seldom noticed. Specific diagnosis is made by detecting the typically pleomorphic organisms in granulocytes in Giemsa-stained blood smears. Leucopenia is also a characteristic of tick-borne fever which is followed by a marked neutropenia. These haematological changes reflect a generalized immunosuppression which results in increased susceptibility to secondary infection. In particular, infection of young lambs may result in tick pyaemia, caused by *Staphylococcus aureus*, a normal commensal of the skin, disseminating in the blood to infect joints, spinal cord and internal organs resulting in a wide variety of clinical signs including lameness, paralysis and ill-thrift.

Control of tick pyaemia is difficult, in part because the incidence of disease can vary markedly between years. Chemoprophylaxis with long-acting penicillin or tetracycline has not generally been found to be practical. If exposure of lambs to heavy parasitism can be delayed until they are a month old the incidence of tick pyaemia can be markedly reduced. One of the most effective ways of achieving this could be with the use of the pour-on pyrethroid preparations to reduce tick infestation in the vulnerable age group.

The other major complication of tick-borne fever occurs when animals are exposed to ticks for the first time when pregnant. This can result in a high incidence of abortion followed by septic metritis resulting in serious mortality. Pregnant animals that have not had previous experience of ticks should therefore never be introduced to tick-infected pastures. Tick-borne fever can predispose to many other infections also such as pasteurellosis and louping ill. In the case of louping ill the incidence of severe disease can be markedly increased by the dual infection but this can be prevented by vaccination against louping ill virus.

INFECTION IN MAN

Louping ill virus infection of man can be serious and is sometimes fatal. Fortunately infection by tick bite is a rare event in the UK and infection is more frequently acquired through handling infected carcases. In addition it should be remembered that during the acute phase of infection the milk of sheep and goats contains high titres of virus and thus any such animals that are milked in endemic areas must be vaccinated.

Occasionally human infection with babesia occurs but generally only splenectomized individuals develop disease. In addition Lyme's disease has become increasingly recognized in the UK as a consequence of tick bite. This disease, caused by infection with *Borrelia* species, is characterized by a local reaction around a tick bite and the subsequent development of polyradiculoneuritis and meningitis.

CHAPTER 16

Footrot

KENTON MORGAN

INTRODUCTION

The degree of lameness tolerated in sheep flocks would be unacceptable in any other species. A stable or kennel with animals hobbling or crawling around would be inconceivable, yet this is a familiar sight on sheep farms. Footrot is still one of the most important and painful causes of lameness in the UK, yet effective control methods were established in 1941 and continue to be recommended reading (Beveridge, 1956). It is also surprising that in the intervening years, there have been few reports published on the efficacy of methods of footrot control under UK conditions (Littlejohn, 1961; Roberts et al., 1972; Thorley et al., 1986).

General foot problems and foot care have been dealt with in an article by Boundy (1979) to which the reader is referred. During the past eight years there have been significant changes in the sheep industry, some of which have favoured the parasite and some the host (Table 16.1).

Table 16.1 Changes in the sheep industry favouring the parasite or host.

Favouring the parasite
  Increased numbers of lowland sheep
  Increased stocking densities
  Winter housing
  Inexperienced farmers

Favouring the host
  The increasing value of individual sheep
  Improvements in nutrition
  Resurrected and novel footbathing agents
  New vaccines
  Improvements in disease recording and veterinary preventative medicine

---

DEFINITIONS

Footrot is the disease caused by infection of the ovine foot with *Bacterioides nodosus* and *Fusobacterium necrophorum*. It occurs as a result of the synergistic interaction between these and other organisms such as *Corynebacterium pyogenes* and susceptible sheep under the right environmental conditions.

This interaction results in a spectrum of disease with variations in the severity of lesions and the proportion of the flock affected. At the extremes of the spectrum are two easily recognized conditions:

(1)   Non-progressive, benign footrot or scald – characterized by inflammation of the interdigital skin and little or no separation or underrunning of the horn. In spite of its name, benign footrot may cause an acute and painful lameness.
(2)   Progressive or virulent footrot – characterized by extensive separation of the horn and the presence of a foul smelling necrotic exudate.

THEORETICAL BASIS OF CONTROL

Following accurate diagnosis, an understanding of the factors producing footrot allows a flexible approach to footrot control (Fig. 16.1)

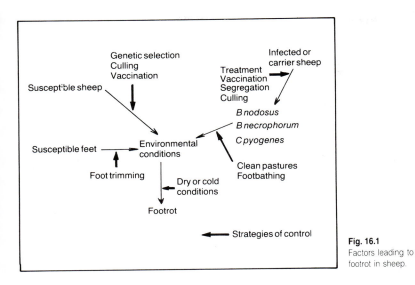

Fig. 16.1
Factors leading to footrot in sheep.

B. NODOSUS

Four features of *B. nodosus* important in disease control are:

(1) It survives for a maximum period of two weeks outside the host.
(2) Virulent strains may be identified by a combination of laboratory tests (production of heat stable proteases, elastase, rough colonies and large numbers of fimbriae).
(3) The fimbrial or serotype specific antigens are important protective immunogens.
(4) The extracellular proteases are important cross-protective antigens.

The laboratory differentiation of virulent and benign strains is not important in the UK.

Fimbrial antigens stimulate an immunity which is serotype specific. This has resulted in the development of multivalent vaccines. Nine major serotypes A–I have been recognized and the most common in the UK are B, D and H. Surveys suggest that although half the farms support multiple serotypes, only 10% of individual sheep are infected with more than one serotype.

Multivalent vaccines tend to suffer changes in differential growth and loss of fimbriae during preparation. Consequently, there has been considerable interest in the preparation of peptide and recombinant DNA vaccines.

A disadvantage of peptide vaccines is that they often lack the tertiary structure necessary to stimulate the production of an antibody which recognizes the native molecule. Recombinant vaccines prepared by cloning the fimbrial gene into *Escherichia coli* have the advantage of producing mature complete fimbriae with the correct antigenic configuration. A recombinant footrot vaccine is currently undergoing clinical trials.

In the long term, the selection pressures introduced by recombinant and peptide vaccines may give rise to strains of *B. nodosus* where the importance of the fimbriae to virulence and immunity is taken over by other antigens.

SUSCEPTIBLE SHEEP

Very little is known about the factors influencing the susceptibility of individual sheep or breeds to infection. Farmers recognize that some individuals in an infected flock develop severe footrot whereas others do not. This has been confirmed by epidemiological studies. In Australia, differences in breed susceptibility are also recognized, with Merinos being most susceptible under conditions of moderate challenge.

SUSCEPTIBLE FEET

Even less is known about the factors responsible for the apparent variation in susceptibility of individual feet on the same sheep. Excessive horn growth may play a role and some shepherds suggest that white feet are particularly susceptible but there is little evidence to support this.

ENVIRONMENTAL CONDITIONS

In Australia, the spread of footrot requires temperatures in excess of 10°C. Similar studies have not been carried out in the UK but it has been suggested that spread may occur at temperatures below 10°C. Traditionally, severe outbreaks were seen in late spring and early autumn but winter housing has been accompanied by severe attacks of footrot between November and January.

EPIDEMIOLOGY

Footrot shows seasonal trends which are influenced by geographical, climatic and managemental factors. An example of the pattern of disease in a winter-housed lowland flock during a year with a wet summer is shown in Fig. 16.2.

A knowledge of the pattern of disease is valuable because it gives the farmer a quantitative assessment of his problem and it allows strategic introduction and correct evaluation of control methods.

Recording systems, an essential part of footrot control, also indicate the pattern of disease. A simple system of recording involves scoring feet O or X in the sequence RF, LF, RH, LH at convenient times such as scanning, shearing and culling. An example of a more sophisticated scoring system is shown in Fig. 16.3.

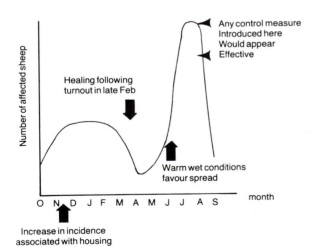

Fig. 16.2
Pattern of footrot in a lowland winter-housed flock.

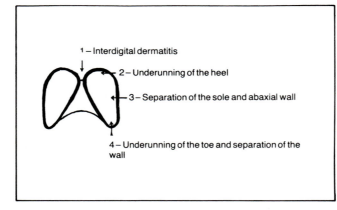

1 – Interdigital dermatitis

2 – Underunning of the heel

3 – Separation of the sole and abaxial wall

4 – Underunning of the toe and separation of the wall

Fig. 16.3
Scoring foot lesions.

STRATEGIES FOR CONTROL (Fig. 16.4)

Control measures aim to prevent colonization of the ovine foot by *B. nodosus* by limiting or preventing the interactions shown in the first figure using a combination of the following strategies:

(1) Reducing the level or removing the challenge with *B. nodosus* by;
    Reducing the number of infected or carrier animals:
    Treatment (a) Chemotherapy (topical, parenteral or oral)
               (b) footparing
    Vaccination
    Segregation
    Culling
    Using clean or uninfected pastures or premises
(2) Increasing the resistance of individual sheep:
    Vaccination
    Selective breeding
(3) Decreasing the susceptibility of individual feet:
    Foot trimming
    Footbathing
(4) Providing environmental conditions which limit the development and spread of disease:
    Using well-drained land
    The use of adequate bedding when housed

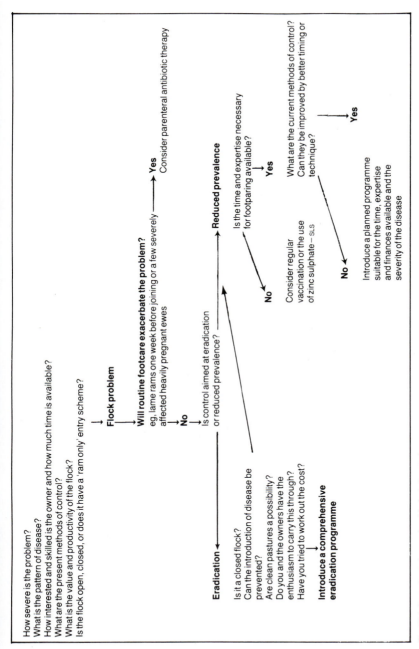

How severe is the problem?
What is the pattern of disease?
How interested and skilled is the owner and how much time is available?
What are the present methods of control?
What is the value and productivity of the flock?
Is the flock open, closed, or does it have a 'ram only' entry scheme?

Flock problem

Will routine footcare exacerbate the problem?
eg, lame rams one week before joining or a few severely
affected heavily pregnant ewes ─────→ **Yes**
Consider parenteral antibiotic therapy
↓ **No**

Is control aimed at eradication
or reduced prevalence?

Eradication ────────── **Reduced prevalence**

Is it a closed flock?
Can the introduction of disease be
prevented?
Are clean pastures a possibility?
Do you and the owners have the
enthusiasm to carry this through?
Have you tried to work out the cost?

**Introduce a comprehensive
eradication programme**

Is the time and expertise necessary
for footpaIring available?
↓ **Yes**

What are the current methods of control?
Can they be improved by better timing or
technique?

No ↓   ┌──→ **Yes**
Consider regular
vaccination or the use   No ↓
of zinc sulphate — SLS   Introduce a planned programme
                               suitable for the time, expertise
                               and finances available and the
                               severity of the disease

Fig. 16.4 Strategies to be employed in footrot control.

EVALUATION OF CONTROL METHODS

Topical chemotherapy

Footbaths and the use of purple sprays are by far the most common forms of topical treatment.

Footbaths

The use of formalin has been advocated for use in footbaths as a result of early studies although moderately good results have been achieved with zinc sulphate. Recently, there has been a renewal of interest in this agent. Zinc sulphate has the advantage of being non-toxic to both shepherd and sheep. It has no odour and, unlike copper sulphate, does not cause fleece staining or the corrosion of galvanized baths.

The comparative efficiency of formalin and zinc sulphate is a subject of considerable debate. Too often in practice this reflects their use in a way which defies all the principles of topical treatment, i.e. that the agent must come into contact with the organism or diseased tissue and must remain in contact with it at an effective concentration for long enough to exert its desired effect, without causing tissue damage. It is therefore unlikely that sheep with overgrown and underrun feet will derive any benefit at all from charging through a murky footbath and being returned directly to a wet pasture – whatever the agent.

Contact between the chemical agent and infected tissue may be achieved by paring, i.e. the removal of horn from underrun parts of the foot to expose all affected areas or by penetration through the skin and horn to the site of infection.

Formalin does not penetrate the horn of the foot even when exposed *in vitro* for five days. So, to exert therapeutic effect, the use of formalin must be preceded by footparing and must be followed by a period of draining and drying on a hard surface.

The importance of treatment before and after bathing was illustrated by two independent studies which showed cure rates of 59% for footparing alone and 35% by simply keeping affected sheep on a slatted floor for 24 hours. The recommended time of immersion in formalin varies from 1 to 10 minutes.

Clinical trials suggest that in most cases 3–5 minutes is adequate, although for severe cases 10 minutes may be necessary. Formalin is irritant and toxic and should not be used at a concentration greater than 5% (preferably 4%) or more frequently than once a week. Formalin is cheap and has been in use for a number of years. Controlled trials suggest a short-term cure of 40–60% following a single treatment. Existing narrow footbaths have been designed for use with formalin and in flocks having a shepherd with the skill and time to pare the foot correctly, improving the efficiency of footbathing by, for example, better drying may be the simplest and cheapest way of improving results.

Zinc sulphate (Golden hoof; Shep Fair Products, Crickhowell) penetrates the hoof. Prior treatment with formalin prevents the uptake of zinc sulphate so they should not be used in rotation.

The hard horn of the ovine foot is 1–2 mm thick and *in vitro* studies suggest that it would take 5 hours for zinc sulphate to penetrate this. Therefore it is unlikely that there is any significant penetration following footbathing in 10% zinc sulphate for 2 minutes. Used in this way, zinc sulphate acts as a surface antibacterial agent like formalin. So footparing, drying and repeated bathing are essential for maximum efficacy. There have been few reports of the efficacy of zinc sulphate under field conditions in the UK but results from Australia and the USA vary from 100% cure to no significant advantage over paring alone.

The penetration of zinc sulphate may be enhanced by increasing the footbathing time or by using a penetrating agent such as the anionic detergents sodium lauryl sulphate (SLS) or Tween 20. One such preparation (Footrite; Veterinary Pharmaceuticals) requires that footbathing be carried out for one hour. In these circumstances footparing is not essential. It has even been suggested that it lowers the efficacy of zinc sulphate–SLS by reducing the horn available for penetration. However, where feet are malformed with thickened horn harbouring pockets of infection, paring is beneficial and is recommended even when using zinc sulphate–SLS. Care should be taken when paring feet as zinc sulphate–SLS tends to exacerbate bleeding. Bleeding should have stopped before the sheep is run through the footbath.

The use of Footrite has resulted in the development of larger footbaths. One of the limiting factors to footbath size is the expense of this agent. The recommended usage is 1 kg per seven sheep (allowing re-use on three occasions) with half the flock being footbathed in a day. Allowing 0.2–0.3 m² per sheep the optimum footbath size can be calculated as follows:

$$\frac{\text{Number of sheep in half the flock}}{\text{Length of working day (hours)}} \times 0.25 \text{ m}^2$$

If the footbath is filled to a height of 5–6 cm, the volume of Footrite can also be calculated (1 kg Footrite is dissolved in 6.4 litres of water). Large footbaths may be constructed in pre-existing concrete yards using removable hurdles. When using zinc sulphate–SLS preparations it is important the following points are observed:

(1) The footbath is easily accessible from the sheep house.
(2) It is sited so as to allow the sheep to run uphill and towards a horizon.
(3) Sheep move through it slowly as surface foaming makes them reluctant to enter the bath.
(4) Wastage is avoided by having solid sides to a height of 50 cm and a drainage exit ramp.
(5) A perimeter ledge should be avoided.

Zinc sulphate–SLS preparations are more toxic than simple zinc sulphate and there are reports of death following its consumption, and conjunctivitis in dogs and sheep following accidental splashing.

In Australia, short-term cure rates of 70–100% have followed the recommended two, 1-hour footbaths with Footrite five days apart. Other studies suggest little long-term advantage over footparing alone. It is likely that in field conditions in the UK repeated bathing will be necessary, particularly in severely affected flocks.

Purple sprays

The active ingredient of these sprays include either dichlorophen (2% and 7.5%), cetrimide, copper naphthenate, oxytetracycline or chlortetracycline. Good cure rates have been reported using 10% dichlorophen but there is little information on the efficacy of the other products.

Parenteral treatment

In screening tests of penicillin, streptomycin, neomycin, oxytetracycline, erythromycin and sulphonamides, only high doses of erythromycin or penicillin with streptomycin were effective in treating footrot. The high dose rates were Streptopen (Glaxovet) 1 ml/2–4 kg, erythromycin 20 mg/kg.

Oral treatment

The efficacy of oral zinc sulphate in the treatment and prevention of footrot is controversial. Dramatic results were obtained in a controlled trial in Greece. Footrot disappeared following oral administration of 0.5 g zinc sulphate for seven weeks. These findings were supported by results from France but were unsubstantiated by trials in New Zealand and the USA. The reason for this discrepancy is unclear.

Vaccination

Sheep may suffer persistent and repeated attacks of footrot. This failure of natural infection to stimulate a protective immune response suggests that footrot is a poor candidate for vaccination–yet two vaccines, Clovax and Footvax (Coopers Animal Health) are currently available in the UK. These whole cell vaccines differ in the serotypes of *B. nodosus* included and the adjuvant employed. There have been few published reports of the efficacy of these vaccines under field conditions in the UK. Clinical trials carried out in Australia claim both therapeutic and prophylactic effects but critical examination of these trials suggests that the degree of immunity varies according to the severity of challenge, that the duration of immunity is short and that severe local reactions occur at the vaccination site. In spite of these deficiencies, the development of effective vaccines is clearly important and deserves further discussion.

Interest in vaccination followed the observation that the bactericidal activity of sheep serum for *B. nodosus* could be enhanced by immunization. The importance of high titres of antibody was confirmed experimentally by the short-term protection provided by the passive transfer of serum to naive animals. Early field trials established that two doses of an oil adjuvant vaccine protected 50–95% of animals for up to 10 weeks. Interestingly, these studies suggested that protection was associated with high titres of antibody to the O or somatic antigen of B. nodosus. They also demonstrated a "therapeutic" effect of vaccination with a decreasing number of affected sheep in the vaccinated group. One disadvantage of these oil adjuvant vaccines was the local tissue reactions which they produced. When used subcutaneously, abscesses of 1–25 cm in diameter were recorded.

The severe chronic local reactions induced by oil adjuvant vaccines resulted in the development of alum absorbed vaccines. Clovax was introduced in the UK in the early 1970s. Clinical trials in the UK showed a significant reduction in the development of clinical footrot in vaccinated animals. In contrast, laboratory studies in Australia suggested that immunity lasted for only 4–8 weeks and the poor results obtained with clinical trials resulted in the withdrawal of alum absorbed vaccines from the Australian market in 1976.

The development of multivalent oil adjuvant vaccines arose from the observation that the fimbriae of B. nodosus were important protective immunogens. Experimentally, oil adjuvant preparations of fimbriated vaccines stimulated a greater antibody response and duration of immunity than alum absorbed vaccines. Even so immunity lasted for only about eight weeks.

When the therapeutic effects of oil adjuvant and alum absorbed vaccines were compared, a significant "cure rate" was obtained with both vaccines. Interestingly, this was not related to the level of antibody to the fimbrial antigen, suggesting either that other antigens are involved in the protective immune response or that the "therapeutic effect" is nonspecific. The early suggestion that protection was associated with the somatic antigen and the more recent observation that proteases are important in cross-protection between different serotypes demonstrate that antigens other than the fimbriae are important in immunity but the nonspecific role of the oil adjuvant vaccine needs clarification. In pigs, for example, post-weaning mortality has been reduced by the use of oil adjuvants alone and a single dose of footrot vaccine elicits a poor antibody response but a significant therapeutic response. Evaluation of the therapeutic effect of vaccination should involve a control group given adjuvant alone.

Vaccination abscesses are a feature of the use of Footvax (Ross and Titterington, 1984; Mulvaney *et al.*, 1984; Glenn *et al.*, 1985). The data sheets warn against the use of Footvax prior to shearing or showing and it is contraindicated in milking sheep where it causes a dramatic fall in yield. In clinical trials vaccination abscesses varied in diameter from 0.5 to 15 cm but were usually within the range 2–5 cm. They occurred in up to 86% of animals and were still apparent 6–12 weeks after injection. One must question whether this is acceptable.

In practice then, multivalent oil adjuvant vaccines may be used prophylactically and therapeutically in the control of footrot. These vaccines cost about £1.50 per initial course and they have the following limitations:

(1)   The therapeutic effect is extremely variable. In Australia cure rates of 70–100% have been reported whereas in more recent controlled trials in New Zealand the figures were −40% to +40% with significant effect in only two of five flocks.

(2)   The duration of immunity is short – 12 weeks at maximum. Vaccination should be timed so that this period of immunity coincides with the period of disease spread. A knowledge of the pattern of disease in the flock is therefore essential. In severely affected flocks it may be necessary to revaccinate at 3–4 monthly intervals.

(3)   Severe vaccination abscesses occur – temporary lameness may occur if the axilla is used as the vaccination site. The owner should be warned.

(4)   As with most vaccines protection is not absolute.

Footparing

Details of footparing are described elsewhere (Littlejohn, 1966/67; Boundy, 1979). When carried out correctly it is a skilled but tiring task and it is therefore essential that the conditions provided should favour the operator.

Important points for footparing include:

(1)   Sharp and appropriate instruments.
(2)   Adequate restraint, e.g. another person, turning crate, "deckchair".
(3)   Well-designed handling facilities, e.g. a curved race running towards the horizon, shelter from the wind and rain.

In controlled trials footparing alone results in a significant cure rate but may also exacerbate lameness in the short term and result in misshapen feet or granuloma formation.
Evidence suggests that in spite of the development of new vaccines and penetrating footbaths, paring will remain an important part of footrot control for the foreseeable future.

Segregation

In theory, the segregation of infected and non-infected sheep allows a footrot-free flock to be established rapidly on the farm. In practice, it is often difficult to identify sheep with healed lesions which still harbour infection. As a result new cases of footrot may appear in the clean flock. This system also presents considerable management problems.

Culling

As the prevalence of footrot decreases in a flock, sheep with feet that appear refractory to control measures and those with deformed feet should be culled.

Use of clean pastures

B. nodosus survives for a maximum of two weeks outside the host and a pasture free of cattle, sheep, goats or deer for two weeks may be considered clean. Where possible, sheep should be moved to clean, dry, grazing following paring and bathing.

Practical aspects of footrot control

The veterinary input to footrot control on different farms will vary considerably but it is important that in each instance the most appropriate and effective strategy is applied.

Considerable thought should be given to eradication programmes and they should not be entered into lightly. They require all the features of PREV medicine.

Planning
Recording
Enthusiasm
Vigilance

An example of an eradication programme:

(1) Fix the starting date a season in advance.
(2) Monitor and record those sheep which develop footrot before the starting date.
(3) Examine all sheep.
Pare all affected feet thoroughly
Treat the most severely affected animals parenterally
Footbath all sheep in zinc sulphate, zinc sulphate–SLS or formalin for the correct period
Allow at least an hour on concrete for drying
Return to clean grazing
Record what you find
Be present yourself for at least some of the time
(4) Repeat footbath once after five days for zinc sulphate–SLS or weekly for four weeks for other agents.
(5) Re-examinine all sheep as in (3) after one month or when changing fields.
(6) Repeat one month later and consider culling persistently infected sheep.
(7) Continue until the flock is footrot free and then maintain regular and comprehensive examination of the feet.

In the absence of a regional or national scheme the eradication of footrot from open infected flocks is a daunting task. The absence of footrot from the list of diseases included in the recent health monitoring scheme is surprising but probably reflects the difficulty in identifying flocks free of footrot on a laboratory basis. State controlled footrot schemes have been in progress in Australia since the early 1950s. They have reduced the number of infected farms in Victoria from 50 to 10%. The cost benefit analysis of a 30-year footrot control scheme in this state has been estimated at about 20 million dollars. Financial losses apart, the new welfare codes also recognize the problem of footrot and it would seem that a national monitoring scheme or at least a cost benefit analysis of footrot control schemes is appropriate.

REFERENCES

Beveridge, W. I. B. (1956). *Veterinary Record* **68**, 963.

Boundy, T. (1979). *In Practice* **1**, 28.

Glenn, A., Carpenter, T. E. & Hird, D. W. (1985). *Journal of American Veterinary Medical Association* **187**, 1009.

Littlejohn, A. I. (1961). *Veterinary Record* **73**, 773.

Littlejohn, A. I. (1966/67). *Veterinary Annual* 1966/67, 71.

Mulvaney, C. J., Jackson, R. & Jopp, A. J. (1984). *New Zealand Veterinary Journal* **32**, 137.

Roberts, D. S., Foster, W. H., Kerry, J. B. & Mc C. Calder, H. A. (1972). *Veterinary Record* **91**, 428.

Ross, A. D. & Titterington, D. M. (1984). *New Zealand Veterinary Journal* **32**, 6.

Stewart, D. J., Clark, B. L., Emery, D. L., Peterson, J. E. & Kortt, A. A. (1985). In *Footrot in Ruminants. Proceedings of a Workshop*, Melbourne, 1985 (eds D. J. Stewart, J. E. Peterson, N. M. McKern & D. L. Emery). CSIRO, 1986.

Thorley, C. M., Kerry, J. B., Mc C. Calder, H. A., Ripley, P. H. & Day, S. E. J. (1985). *Footrot in Ruminants. Proceedings of a Workshop.* Melbourne, 1985 (eds D. J. Stewart, J. E. Peterson, N. M. McKern & D. L. Emery). CSIRO.

CHAPTER 17

Differential Diagnosis of Nervous Diseases of Sheep

RICHARD BARLOW

INTRODUCTION

Among the common domestic species, sheep are noteworthy for the variety of neurological disorders of differing aetiologies to which they are susceptible. In many of these conditions treatment of the individual is of limited value, but rapid accurate diagnosis is essential if flock problems amenable to prophylaxis or change in management practices are to be identified.

Specific diagnosis in most instances is a laboratory procedure involving histology of the nervous system, sometimes supported by microbiology or chemistry. The value of these examinations depends on the care with which samples are taken. The selection of samples and their treatment both depend upon the results of the clinical examination and the range of the diagnostic options to be considered.

CLINICAL EXAMINATION

Obtaining a full and accurate description of the complaint is essential. It is best to start before approaching the flock, as one can then give the shepherd undivided attention and so gain time later for specific points to be developed or checked for accuracy. It is prudent to be aware that a diagnosis may already have formed in the shepherd's mind and his observations unconsciously interpreted so as to fit that diagnosis; this could be misleading. In taking the history, particular attention should be paid to the age, sex and diet of affected sheep, any recent dietary changes and management practices such as marking, clipping, dipping or worming.

Examine the environment in which the disease occurred (see Table 17.1).

Examine the affected animals undisturbed in their usual flock surroundings. This will allow comparative assessments of the body condition and any alterations in social and grazing behaviour, stance and locomotor activity.

HEAD CARRIAGE

Particular attention should be paid to head carriage. Excessive attentiveness may be caused by hyperaesthesia or defective vision. Head tilt (rotation about the long axis) may indicate inner/middle ear infection or a lesion in the upper medulla, which is usually on the same side as the lower ear. Lateral deviation of the head may be a result of unilateral blindness, while vertical aversions (up or down) may occur with generalized brain swelling, cerebral or cerebellar cortical lesions, malacias or meningitis (Fig. 17.1).

Head tremor may be vertical or horizontal and is almost always of low frequency and small amplitude. It is indicative of pathological changes in the cerebellum or diencephalon. High frequency low amplitude head tremor is observed in some cases of meningoencephalitis in which it may be accompanied by chorea (hyperkinesia). Fine tremor of head

Table 17.1 Checklist of environmental factors which may cause disease.

Nature and quantity of feed
Sources of water
Evidence of recent applications of fertilizer or weed killer
Proximity of dumps
Knowledge of trace element status of the locality

Fig. 17.1
Daft lamb disease. Note the wide stance and the "stargazing" carriage of the head. The tear scald on the right cheek indicates the persistence of the latter. Such lambs are prone to conjunctivitis and when bottle fed may also develop middle ear infections.

and ears may also be seen with gross intracranial malformations in the newborn.

Compulsive circling movements may indicate a brainstem or cerebellar lesion on the side to which the animal turns, or a cerebral lesion which is usually on the opposite side.

SPECIAL SENSES AND LOCOMOTION

A cautious approach to the flock will provide further impressions as to the visual and acoustic acuity of the affected animal. It may be possible to observe the ease with which it can get to its feet and move off (Fig. 17.2). In the initial moments of movement, knuckling of fetlocks or circling may be most readily observed. Such abnormalities may be seen in swayback and are said to be characteristic of visna. Movement of the flock at a slow walk will reveal intention tremor,

Fig. 17.2
"Kangaroo gait" is a recently reported disorder which develops about a month after lambing, usually in big ewes nursing twins or triplets. Note how the weight is taken on the hind legs, forelimb movements being weak and uncoordinated.

incoordination or ataxia, e.g. in louping ill. Acceleration to a brisk sustained trot will show up any progressive locomotor weakness – a characteristic feature of delayed swayback (Fig. 17.3).

Collectively, these observations should help to eliminate a number of functional metabolic disorders and musculoskeletal conditions. They should also determine to a large extent whether there is likely to be a focal lesion located either in the brain, eye, ear, spinal cord or peripheral nerve.

PHYSICAL EXAMINATION

Further examination is best conducted after the sheep has been allowed to settle in a loose box in which the illumination can be controlled. Observe carefully the response to your approach; apprehension and trembling occur in scrapie (Fig. 17.4) and some encephalitides, while bruxism, dullness and depression are features of focal symmetrical encephalomalacia, advanced meningitis and other conditions accompanied by acute brain swelling. Observe the carriage and symmetry of the head. Bulging of the cheek caused by retention of cud, lingual paralysis, drooping of the ear or eyelid are indicative of facial paralysis and suggest lesions involving the facial nerve, or its adjacent nuclei on the medulla on the affected

Fig. 17.3
Delayed swayback can develop in thriving lambs up to about three months of age. Hind leg weakness and ataxia are characteristic features and are exacerbated by exercise.

Fig. 17.4
Scrapie. Suffolk
sheep standing apart
from the flock in poor
condition with wool
loss over the back
and shoulders. Note
the dull vacant facial
expression. Its
movements were also
uncoordinated.

side, e.g., listeral encephalitis (Fig. 17.5).

Nystagmus, i.e. oscillatory movements of the eyeballs, is associated with lesions in the brainstem, the vestibular apparatus or cerebellum. Unequal sized pupils are suggestive of damage to the hypothalamus or the cervical sympathetic portion of the autonomic nervous system.

Application of the photomotor reflex will detect lesions in the eye, optic or oculomotor nerve, while the corneal and eye protection reflexes test for lesions in the trigeminal and facial nerves. An assessment of obstacle avoidance after blindfolding

Fig. 17.5
An early case of
listerial encephalitis.
Note slight head
aversion and the
swelling of the cheek
due to retention of
cud. (Photograph
courtesy of W. T.
Appleyard)

either or both eyes is, however, the most effective method of testing for blindness. Use of the ophthalmoscope and mydriatics will allow the contents of the eye to be examined.

In relation to neurological disease the condition of the retina is of particular value. Excessive reflectivity and narrowed retinal vessels indicate retinal atrophy, as in bright blindness associated with chronic bracken poisoning. Papilloedema, a swelling of the optic disc with blurring of its edges, may occur in conditions in which intracranial pressure is raised.

In sheep, the cutaneous and pedal reflexes are probably the most useful means of testing local spinal reflex arcs. If the stimuli applied are painful these reflexes can also be used to assess the integrity of spinothalamic and motor pathways in the spinal cord and so locate focal spinal lesions – such as spinal abscess or vertebral subluxations. Spinal abscesses are not uncommon in lambs and often solitary at C7/T1 (Fig. 17.6), or in the lumbar region where they may be a consequence of infection gaining entry at docking. Subluxations of cervical vertebrae with local contusion of the spinal cord have been reported in young adults and are probably the result of fighting.

The results of the clinical examination should establish whether or not a neurological condition is present, whether it is a problem of the individual or the flock and whether the lesion is likely to be localized to a particular division of the nervous system. This may be sufficient for a diagnosis to be made. It would be prudent to have this diagnosis confirmed by laboratory examination, especially if several animals are affected.

Fig. 17.6
This well, thriving lamb suddenly developed complete posterior paralysis. A solitary abscess was present in the C7/T1 intervertebral articulation, pointing dorsally into the vertebral canal.

CONFIRMATION OF CLINICAL DIAGNOSIS

Many neurological diseases of sheep are of a generalized nature and even if a solitary lesion is suspected it is desirable to remove the entire central nervous system, appropriate samples of dorsal root ganglia and peripheral nerves and also representative portions of the autonomic nervous system. These operations must be done carefully, as stretching or rough handling produce histological artefacts which can be misinterpreted as pathological change.

When dealing with a flock problem it is better to kill an advanced case (and, if possible, also an early case) rather than rely on a sheep which has been dead for some time and may have advanced autolytic changes. If it is considered appropriate to collect cerebrospinal fluid this is more readily achieved from the live anaesthetized animal than a dead one. A

Fig. 17.7
Position of the saw-cuts on the skull for removal of the brain.

1.5-inch 21 gauge needle is usually sufficient to penetrate the cisterna magna if the sheep is put over a bale with the head low and flexed and the vertebral column kept straight. The flow of cerebrospinal fluid can be assisted by gentle pressure on the jugular veins. Minimal suction should be applied to the syringe if rupture of a blood vessel is to be avoided.

For euthanasia, barbiturate anaesthetics are satisfactory. Chloroform or ether should be avoided as they affect the quality of histological preparations. Shooting or stunning with a captive bolt pistol, of course, renders the tissue virtually useless. If necropsy is to be delayed for any length of time, immediate decapitation will allow the blood and cerebrospinal fluid to drain away and help delay post-mortem changes. Removal to a cool place will also help, but freezing should be avoided.

Fig. 17.8
The roof of the cranial vault has been prised off and the meninges removed. The forceps indicate the position of the transverse fibrous band, the tentorium cerebelli, which must be wholly and carefully removed before the brain can be extracted without damage.

POST-MORTEM EXAMINATION

In carrying out the examination for a suspected neurological disease the general post-mortem examination should not be neglected, proper attention being paid also to the condition of the viscera, muscles, bones and joints. It is, however, easiest if the brain and spinal cord are removed before opening the body cavities.

The head is removed by section through the allanto-occipital space. It is then skinned and the cranial vault sawn through with a tenon saw using a diamond-shaped configuration of saw cuts (Fig. 17.7). Laterally these follow the line of the medial border of the occipital condyles and anteriorly should be in line with and about 2.5 cm behind the supraorbital process. The "lid of the brain case" can then be prised off to expose the dura mater; this is then removed with scalpel and forceps, taking care to completely excise the thick fibrous band, the tentorium cerebelli, which separates the cerebrum from the cerebellum (Fig. 17.8). This is a convenient point at which small samples can be removed cleanly with fine pointed scissors for microbiological or biochemical examination. Then by severing the cranial nerves the brain can be released from the cranium. If required, the pituitary, trigeminal ganglia, eyes and optic nerves can now be dissected out and the middle ear examined by opening the osseous bulla of the petrous temporal bone.

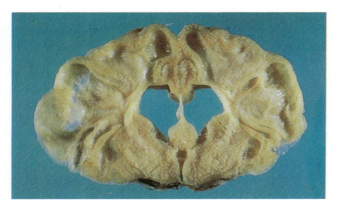

Fig. 17.9
Transverse slice through the brain of a congenital case of swayback. Note the dilated ventricle and the gelatinous transformation and cavitation of the gyral cores. These changes are seen in about 50% of congenital cases but are not found in the delayed form of the disease.

Table 17.2 Some common ovine neurological diseases by age.

Age group	Disease	Associated with infection	Environment	Management	Comment
Before term	Toxoplasmosis	+	+	++	Contamination of feed with cat faeces
	Chlamydiosis	+	+	+	Lambing pens, retention of surviving lambs for breeding flock
	Border disease	+	+	+	Retention/introduction of persistently infected animals at tupping time
Birth–7 days	Border disease	+	+	+	Retention/introduction of persistently infected animals at tupping time
	Congenital swayback	–	++	+	Mild winter, pasture improvements leading to low Cu^{2+} status
	Daft lamb disease	–	+	++	In breeding
	Brain abscess/spinal abscess	+	+	++	Navel ill/dirty lambing pens. Tick-borne fever Poor docking/castration techniques
	Bacterial meningitis	+	+	++	Navel ill/dirty lambing pens
	Tetanus	+	+	++	Navel ill/dirty lambing pens Poor docking/castration techniques

Age	Condition				Comments/action
7 days–3 months	Focal symmetrical encephalomalacia	+	−	++	Inadequate clostridial vaccination programme
	Delayed swayback	−	++	+	Low Cu^{2+} status
	Listeriosis	+	+	++	Silage feeding/indoor lambing
	Louping ill	+	++	++	Tick-borne. Control by vaccination/management practices
3 months–2 years	Coenuriasis	+	+	++	Control/worm dogs
	Polio-encephalomalacia (CCN)	−	+	+	Increase roughage component of diet
	Hepatic encephalopathy	−	+	+	Hepatotoxins. Cu^{2+} poisoning. Examine diet
Over 2 years	Cervical subluxation	−	−	+	Fighting
	Listeriosis	+	+	++	Strong association with feeding poor silage
	Brain abscess	+	−	+	Fighting?
	Scrapie	+	−	+	Devise culling strategies

With the body of the sheep supported over a bale or an old chair, the skin and muscles of the back can be reflected to expose the vertebral column. The arches of the vertebrae are removed with bone cutting forceps and the spinal cord released by severing the peripheral nerve roots, where possible at a point just distal to the dorsal root ganglia.

The sheep is then turned over on to its back and the autonomic nervous system and peripheral nerves sampled during the general post-mortem examination. The autonomic nervous system is most easily located before removal of the viscera. The thoracic chain lies subpleurally alongside the bodies of the vertebrae and can be dissected out caudally to the coeliaco mesenteric ganglion adjacent to the adrenal gland and cranially to the caudal cervical ganglion and beyond into the neck. Adequate lengths of appropriate peripheral nerves should be dissected out without applying tension and allowed to adhere to pieces of thin card which can be labelled and the proximal and distal extremities indicated.

The samples should all be placed without further dissection in a wide-necked container with an adequate volume (10–20 times that of the tissue) of fixative. For most purposes 10% formol saline or 10% formalin with 1% anhydrous calcium chloride is satisfactory. Phosphate buffered formalin is not appropriate where myelinopathic disorders, e.g. swayback or Border disease, are suspected as it tends to form soluble soaps with the products of myelin degeneration. For eyes, Davidson's fixative (formaldehyde 20 parts, glacial acetic acid 10 parts, methylated spirits 30 parts, distilled water 30 parts) is preferred. Ideally, fixation should be allowed to proceed for several days before transmission to the laboratory for further processing, but in an emergency samples can be despatched immediately if the brain is supported by absorbent cotton wool and the containers used are leak proof (Fig. 17.9).

OCCULT DISEASE

So far, only examination of the animal with clinically suspected neurological disease has been considered. Experience, however, has shown that in cases of sudden death histological examination of the central nervous system can provide supporting evidence for a diagnosis of pulpy kidney disease.

Also, examination of the central nervous system of stillborn lambs and aborted foetuses can be a valuable diagnostic procedure for conditions such as toxoplasmosis, chlamydial abortion and Border disease, providing autolysis has not reached the stage of liquefaction. As foetal tissues are very easily damaged during removal, even if autolysis is absent, preliminary hardening and fixation by perfusion through the left ventricle, abdominal aorta or umbilical artery may be considered. An outlet for the perfusate must be provided in the jugular or femoral vein. For foetal perfusion formol ammonium bromide is a very useful fixative.

CONCLUSIONS

Careful recording and description of the clinical observations followed by a painstaking post-mortem examination are advocated. In the differential diagnosis of disorders of the ovine nervous system three factors appear to be of prime importance; the environment, the management and the age of animals affected (see Table 17.2).

ACKNOWLEDGEMENT

Thanks are due to Mr D. Gunn for the reproduction of some of the figures from cine-film.

CHAPTER 18

Caprine Arthritis-Encephalitis

MICHAEL DAWSON

INTRODUCTION

In recent years caprine arthritis-encephalitis (CAE) has emerged as a significant virus disease of goats in several countries which have dairy goat industries based on breeds of European origin.

The causative lentivirus produces a persistent but subclinical infection in most individuals. If disease does occur, it is associated with a progressive inflammation in one or more organ or tissue systems, namely joints, bursae, brain, spinal cord, lungs and udder (Fig. 18.1). There are distinct similarities with maedi-visna of sheep, not only clinically because of the nature and distribution of lesions, but the causative viruses, both being lentiviruses, are also closely related. CAE can be regarded as the caprine equivalent of maedi-visna.

CAE virus was first isolated in Britain in 1982 from an arthritic goat. Although a serological survey in 1984 indicated that the prevalence of infection was low (4.3%), certain findings gave rise for some concern over the future of the disease here. There was evidence of recently introduced infection by the purchase of animals in a number of infected herds and more than one in five larger herds (more than 13 adult goats) were infected.

Fig. 18.1
Target organs for
development of
lesions in CAE.

Although few cases have been described in Britain, this disease should not be underestimated. In countries where it is established (seropositive reactor rates of 65–81% in limited surveys of goats in Canada, France, Norway, Switzerland and the USA) CAE is recognized as a source of economic loss to the dairy goat industry. Also, with a disease where one of the clinical presentations is a progressive and sometimes crippling arthritis, control is desirable on welfare grounds.

Many goatkeepers in the UK are aware of the potential seriousness of CAE, not least because of the possible damage to their export sales, and already screen their herds periodically for evidence of CAE virus antibodies. The British Goat Society has embarked upon a voluntary CAE monitoring scheme which requires periodic blood sampling of participating herds. CAE accreditation can be gained through MAFF's Sheep and Goat Health Scheme.

CAE VIRUS-ASSOCIATED DISEASE

CAE virus was originally associated with two forms of disease in the USA, an encephalitis of young kids and an arthritis of mature goats. More recently there have been reports of an indurative mastitis affecting CAE virus infected goats and occasionally a progressive interstitial pneumonitis can produce signs of chronic respiratory disease.

ARTHRITIS

The onset of clinical arthritis rarely occurs before sexual maturity and is usually, but not always, insidious. Carpal joints are primarily affected, followed by hocks and stifles (Figs 18.2 and 18.3). Lameness need not be apparent, even when joints are grossly enlarged, but if present it can vary in severity and move from joint to joint. The atlantal and supraspinous bursae may also be enlarged. Cases are afebrile and appetite is maintained but there is gradual loss of condition which is reflected in the quality of the hair coat. Some cases can progress rapidly, especially those associated with acute-onset lameness but others follow a more prolonged course characterized by alternating periods of relapse and remission.

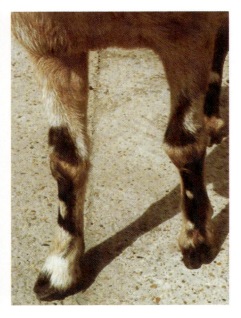

Fig. 18.2
Enlarged left carpus, of several months duration, in a 4-year-old Anglo-Nubian male. Lameness in this leg was periodic.

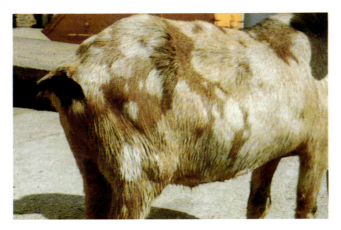

Fig. 18.3
Swelling on the
lateral aspect of the
right stifle indicating
a developing arthritis
which had been
clinically apparent for
about one month.
Lameness had been
constant since onset.

ENCEPHALITIS

Although all ages of goat can be affected, encephalitis usually occurs in kids aged 1–4 months and the signs presented are dependent on the location of the lesions within the central nervous system. Hindlimb or tetraparesis, the most dramatic and frequently encountered manifestation of encephalitis, follows the development of spinal cord lesions, whereas evidence of brain involvement may be less apparent but can include blindness, head tilt and tremor, opisthotonos and torticollis. Cases usually progress to recumbency over a period of days to weeks and require euthanasia; recovery, although recorded, is rare.

INDURATIVE MASTITIS

Indurative mastitis may ultimately prove to be the most economically significant component of CAE. In a Swiss investigation, cases of udder induration outnumbered those of carpal arthritis in 5 of 11 herds studied. All 16 females were affected in one herd where there had been a pronouced drop in milk production. A remarkable feature of this disease is that it can occur before puberty. The diffuse or nodular indurative changes tend to develop deep in the udder tissue initially and gradually extend. The milk appears normal and mastitis may not be suspected by the owner as the cause of a gradual drop in milk yield.

PROGRESSIVE PNEUMONIA

Subclinical lesions of an interstitial pneumonitis, similar to ovine maedi, have been described in CAE virus infected goats of all ages in which the major presenting signs may be of arthritis or encephalitis. However, chronic respiratory disease, usually associated with a progressive weight loss over several months, can occur in the absence of clinical arthritis or encephalitis.

Characteristic of all the syndromes associated with CAE, with the possible exception of some encephalitis cases, are the lack of fever and the maintenance of appetite and an alert disposition.

DIAGNOSIS OF INFECTION

CAE virus infected goats are persistent virus carriers and are capable of transmitting infection irrespective of their clinical status. Identification of subclinical carriers, desirable for control purposes (see later), can be achieved in most cases by serology. Two tests, the agar gel immunodiffusion test and the enzyme-linked immunosorbent assay (ELISA), are used to detect antibody. The close antigenic similarities of CAE and maedi-visna viruses enables an antigen prepared from either to be used for both infections. In the UK, the agar gel immunodiffusion test for CAE actually employs maedi-visna virus antigen: the validity of the test was demonstrated in a comparative trial using both CAE and maedi-visna virus derived antigens.

As with maedi-visna, the period to seroconversion with CAE is prolonged and variable. Colostral antibody can be detected in kids' sera up to 2–3 months of age but active seroconversion may not be detectable for several months, or even years, following natural infection and may be inversely proportional to the severity of challenge. The majority of kids infected in the immediate post-natal period will be seropositive by 1 year old and most will retain their reactor status. The incidence of persistently or periodically seroneg-ative infected goats is not known but obviously such animals will confound attempts to control infection in herds where segregation of seropositives and seronegatives is being attempted.

DIAGNOSIS OF DISEASE

Owners of seropositive goats will probably be alert to the early signs of the CAE-associated syndromes:

(1)   Swollen joints and bursae with or without lameness in adults.
(2)   Abnormal gait, posture, head carriage affecting mainly young kids.
(3)   Gradual decline in milk yield.
(4)   Progressive ill-thrift and laboured breathing.

If signs are encountered in a herd with unknown seriological status, it would be advisable to blood sample as many goats over 6 months old as possible to determine whether the herd is infected, and if so, to what degree. Clinical disease is more likely to occur in those herds with a high prevalence of seropositives.

TO AID FURTHER DIAGNOSIS

Arthritis

Examination of synovial fluid aspirates may be rewarding, although the composition and appearance is variable depending on the stage of the disease. If there is active inflammation, the fluid may be red-brown with a cell count of $1–20 \times 10^3$ per mm^3 and a Giemsa-stained smear will reveal

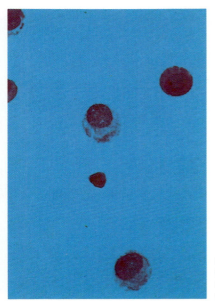

Fig. 18.4
Giemsa-stained smear of synovial fluid aspirate from an
arthritic joint demonstrating predominant presence of
mononuclear cells.

around 90% mononuclear cells (Fig. 18.4). Locally produced
viral antibody may also be detectable in the fluid and thus
indicate recent inflammation. In remission the fluid is clear
and the cell count $1–5 \times 10^2$ per mm^3. Radiography will
detect new bone formation and mineralization of periarticular
connective tissues (Fig. 18.5).

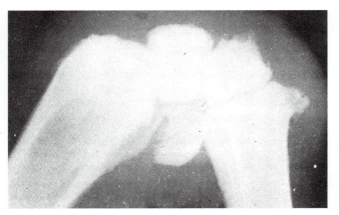

Fig. 18.5
Lateral radiograph of
arthritic carpal joint
from a 4-year-old
British Saanen
female.

At necropsy, the periarticular tissues are thickened and fibrous, and the synovial membrane reddened and inflamed (Fig. 18.6). The synovial fluid may contain fibrin tags. As with all the syndromes of the complex, histological examination is required to confirm the disease and typically this reveals synovial villus hypertrophy, sub-synovial mononuclear cell infiltration and hyperplasia, and sometimes focal areas of necrosis within the synovial membrane or surrounding connective tissues.

Bacterial arthritides should be considered in the differential diagnosis. "Joint-ill" as a sequelae to omphalophlebitis is restricted to kids. In the UK, neither mycoplasma nor chlamydia have been associated with arthritis, though the latter has been recovered from sheep joints. Both are usually associated with acute systemic febrile disease in younger stock, which can be epizootic.

Encephalitis

Clinical signs, age and a herd history of infection are strongly suggestive of CAE encephalitis. Blood biochemical and haematological parameters are within normal ranges but protein content of cerebrospinal fluid may be elevated (more than 40 mg per 100 ml), as may the cell count (again, mononuclear greater than 4×10^3 per mm^3). Histological lesions in the central nervous system consist of multiple perivascular foci of

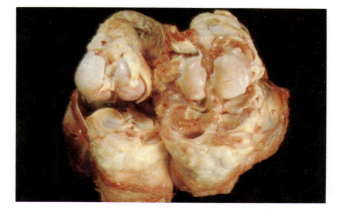

Fig. 18.6
Opened left and right stifle joints of the Anglo-Nubian shown in Fig. 18.2. The left joint is grossly normal but the synovial membrane in the right joint is reddened and inflamed. There is gross thickening of the periarticular connective tissue.

lymphocytes and macrophages in the white matter of the brain and cervical and lumbosacral segments of the spinal cord, commonly associated with demyelination.

In differential diagnosis bacterial meningitis, listeriosis, swayback, cerebrocortical necrosis, spinal trauma, abscessation and possibly lead poisoning should be considered.

Indurative mastitis

A herd history of infection, or possibly clinical arthritis and/or encephalitis would indicate the possibility of an indurative mastitis being the cause of falling milk yield in an individual that was alert with a good appetite – especially if the milk quality is unchanged and bacterial examination fails to identify more familiar causes of mastitis. The diffuse and sometimes nodular indurative changes may be detected by careful udder palpation. Should such a case ultimately be examined post-mortem, several blocks of udder tissue should be taken for histology. The inflammatory changes are similar in character to those in joints and the central nervous system.

Progressive pneumonia

Clinical chronic respiratory disease is probably the most infrequent presentation of CAE virus infection. Progressive dyspnoea and weight loss are indicative but the diagnosis again requires gross post-mortem and histological examination. The lungs are uniformly enlarged with a grey/pink discoloration. Lesions are similar to those of maedi–interstitial pneumonitis consisting of mononuclear cell infiltration and hyperplasia, septal fibrosis and alveolar epithelization. Unlike maedi, the presence of a proteinaceous fluid with alveolar lumina has been described.

TRANSMISSION

Infected colostrum and milk are the most important vehicles of CAE virus transmission. In goat husbandry it has become quite common practice to store, and sometimes pool, frozen colostrum for batch feeding to kids. This, together with the batch feeding of pooled milk, has been suggested as the main reason for the high incidence of infection in the USA. From the herd details available from the UK survey there was also evidence to associate higher within-herd prevalences of infection with such feeding policies. Lateral transmission may possibly occur under conditions of intensive management but rarely at pasture.

No evidence exists of semen transmission but the subject has not been comprehensively studied nor, in the course of epidemiological studies, was there evidence to suggest that brief physical contact with infected males resulted in transmission. In-utero transmission, if it occurs, is a rare event. Although blood borne, CAE virus exists as "dormant" DNA provirus in a small fraction of circulating monocytes and the transfer of small quantities of blood probably represents a low risk of transmission.

CONTROL

As with maedi-visna, in the absence of curative therapy or vaccinal prophylaxis, the approach to controlling CAE virus infection is to limit and preferably to attempt to eliminate transmission. The Ministry of Agriculture's Sheep and Goat Health Scheme is open to goat herds.

In an infected herd, strict attention must be paid to the usage of colostrum and milk. An approach that has been advocated for herds with more than a few reactors, is to assume that no colostrum or milk is safe, regardless of the serological status of the donors. Kids should be removed and separated from their mother at birth and fed uninfected colostrum (for example from an established reactor-free herd), bovine colostrum or as a last resort heat-treated colostrum of unknown status (colostrum which has been heated to 56°C and held at this temperature for one hour); such heat treatment will greatly reduce, if not completely inactivate, virus infectivity without denaturing the immunoglobulin content. Kids can subsequently be fed pasteurized cows' milk. A group of kids so reared should be serologically monitored in order that any reactors can be detected as early as possible; that is, in the event of any having become infected despite control attempts.

If the number of reactors in a herd is low and kids have received only their dams' colostrum/milk then the option exists of splitting the herd into "clean" and seropositives on the basis of periodic herd tests. Clinically healthy reactors need not be culled provided facilities exist for them to be managed as a physically separate group which has no direct contact with the seronegative goats. All progeny of reactors should be managed with the infected goats, regardless of their serological status, because of the exposure to infection via their dams' milk. Any unborn kids can be salvaged by the previously described methods. Management of two such groups should be organized so that the "clean" groups are attended before the infected and each group should have their own utensils. If the herd is milked through a parlour, the same principle applies; the first of the infected group should not enter the parlour until the last of the clean group has left.

It is obviously important to minimize the risk of re-infection from exposure to outside sources. Particular care should be taken over stock purchase, preferably buying only from herds which have been tested regularly and remained free of reactors. Many goat keepers with small herds are dependent on the use of males from other herds. In such cases artificial insemination may eventually provide the answer. However, to date the service only exists on a limited scale in the UK. Because of the unlikely event of transmission occurring, it may be necessary to take a calculated risk and use a male of unknown status.

Owners who are attempting control of CAE, and who regularly attend shows with their goats, must check the serological status of their herds at regular intervals to detect evidence of introduced infection.

Milking competitions pose a particular problem and precautions should be taken by the "stripping-out" stewards to prevent the carry-over of milk from udder to udder. It has been fairly common at shows to offer milk collected in milking trials for feeding to kids. Such a practice presents an unacceptable and unnecessary transmission risk and should be strongly discouraged. Even if the milk has been collected from the kid's own dam in a milking competition, it should

(1980). *American Journal of Pathology* **100**, 443.

Dawson, M. (1985). *Proceedings of the EC Slow Virus Workshop,* Edinburgh, 1983. CEC publications, Report EUR 8076 EV, 233.

Dawson, M. (1988). *Journal of Comparative Pathology* **99**, 401.

Dawson, M. (1989). *Veterinary Annual* **29**, 98.

Dawson, M., Jeffrey, M., Chasey, D., Venables, C. & Sharp, J. M. (1983). *Veterinary Record* **112**, 319.

Dawson, M. & Wilesmith, J. W. (1985). *Veterinary Record* **117**, 86.

Kennedy-Stoskopf, S., Narayan, O. & Strandberg, J. D. (1985). *Journal of Comparative Pathology* **95**, 609.

Norman, S. & Smith, M. C. (1983). *Journal of the American Veterinary Medical Association* **182**, 1342.

Oliver, R. E., Adams, D. S., Gorham, J. R., Julian, A. F., McNiven, R. A. & Muir, J. (1982). *New Zealand Veterinary Journal* **30**, 147.

Oliver, R. E., Cathcart, A., McNiven, R. A., Poole, W. & Robati, G. (1985). *Veterinary Record* **116**, 83.

Robinson, W. F. (1981). *Australian Veterinary Journal* **57**, 127.

Soningo, P., Alizon, M., Staskus, K., Klatzmann, D., Cole, S., Danos, O., Retzel, E., Tiollais, P., Haase, A. T. & Wain-Hobson, S. (1985). *Cell* **42**, 369.

Zwahlen, R., Aeschbacher, M., Balcer, T., Stucki, M., Wyder-Walther, M., Weiss, M. & Steck, F. (1983) *Schweizer Archiv Für Tierheilkunde* **125**, 281.

CHAPTER 19

Parasitic Skin Diseases of Sheep

BILL APPLEYARD AND HARRY BAILIE

INTRODUCTION

A wide range of skin parasites can affect sheep (Table 19.1), with resultant loss or damage to fleece and economic loss associated with impaired production. Some parasites are important in their own right and some are more important as vectors of other infections. The general clinical signs, which are irritation, fleece loss and dermatitis, are common to many infestations and laboratory examinations may be required to establish an accurate diagnosis. Some non-parasitic diseases, such as dermatophilosis or scrapie, have behavioural signs and skin lesions which resemble parasitic infestation. Fleece loss, especially during winter months, has a severe effect on affected sheep and their resistance to cold stress.

CLINICAL EXAMINATION

When investigating outbreaks of skin disease in sheep it may be useful to view the flock from some distance in order that aberrant behaviour may be detected. Note should be taken of itchiness, stamping of feet, restlessness or attempts by the

Table 19.1 Major parasitic diseases of the skin of sheep in the UK.

Disease	Cause	Main signs
Pediculosis	Biting lice (*Damalinia ovis*) Sucking lice (*Linognathus ovillus*)	Irritation, rubbing, loss of fleece. Debility in severe cases. Mainly winter
Sheep scab	Mites (*Psoroptes ovis*)	Marked irritation, rubbing, nibble reflex, yellow or dark crusts in wool. Moist lesions. Mainly winter; milder, less obvious disease in summer
Chorioptic mange	Mites (*Chorioptes ovis*)	Irritation, biting at feet. Thickening and wrinkling of skin of affected areas; brisket, scrotum, lower limbs. Mainly winter
Cutaneous myiasis	Blowfly larvae (various species)	Restlessness, inappetence, moist foul-smelling lesions with maggots visible. Summer
Headfly	*Hydrotaea irritans*	Broken heads, open wounds especially at base of horns. Restlessness, irritation about head. Summer
Keds	*Melophagus ovinus*	Irritation, rubbing, loss of fleece. Anaemia in extreme cases. Mainly winter
Ticks	*Ixodes ricinus*	Tick-associated disease may be the main sign

sheep to attack areas of their bodies.

The proportion of the flock which is affected can be estimated and particular individuals may be taken for closer examination. Flock history is of importance, particularly the recent purchase of sheep, and time of year is often relevant.

Individual sheep should be carefully examined and the character and distribution of fleece loss and any skin lesions noted as well as general body condition. Conditions such as blowfly strike will be readily diagnosed at this stage but others, particularly those involving mites, will require further investigation, including examination of skin scrapings.

It is important that the samples are collected correctly (see below) and that a full history accompanies the submission to the laboratory.

TICKS AND TICK-BORNE DISEASES

Several species of tick have been reported from sheep in Great Britain but by far the most important is the castor bean tick, *Ixodes ricinus*, which occurs widely throughout Britain especially in rough areas where lank vegetation provides shelter for the ticks when off the animal. Ticks will feed on most mammals which makes eradication virtually impossible.

Ixodes is a three-host tick which means that each stage, larva, nymph and adult, feeds on a different host, detaching and moulting between hosts.

Heavy burdens of ticks cause loss of condition but the most important consequence of tick infestation is the transmission of bacterial, viral or protozoal diseases which may cause severe losses. Many such diseases occur throughout the world and those most important in Great Britain are summarized in Table 19.2.

Tick-borne fever, caused by a rickettsia, *Ehrlichia phagocytophilia*, is important in increasing the susceptibility of affected animals to other diseases including louping ill, which is also tick transmitted.

Tick pyaemia, a staphylococcal infection, may result from skin organisms gaining access to the body via the tick bites and this too may be predisposed to by the immunosuppressive effect of tick-borne fever.

While the presence of ticks in an area is usually well known, on occasion problems have occurred in new areas, for example, where cattle have been brought from an infected area with ticks attached to them. If the vegetation in the new area is suitable, a local nucleus of tick infestation, possibly infected with tick-borne diseases, may become established in a previously tick-free area.

Table 19.2 Diseases transmitted by *Ixodes ricinus* to sheep in the UK.

Disease	Cause	Main features
Tick-borne fever	*Rickettsia phagocytophilia*	Affects lambs and previously unexposed older sheep. High fever, dullness, anorexia, loss of condition followed by recovery or by louping-ill or tick pyaemia. Pregnant ewes abort and rams may be temporarily infertile
Louping-ill	Virus	Lambs mainly affected, also adults bought in from tick-free areas. Pyrexia, dullness, anorexia, salivation, head shaking, muscular tremors in neck and limbs leading to rigidity. Typical jerky gait, fits, incoordination, paralysis. Usually fatal when nervous signs appear
Tick pyaemia	*Staphylococcus pyogenes*	Affects lambs, often following tick-borne fever. Signs vary depending on areas in which lesions develop, e.g. joint ill, spinal or brain abscesses giving paralysis, incoordination, etc.

PEDICULOSIS (LICE)

There are two main groups of lice: biting lice and sucking lice, both of which are found on sheep in Britain. *Linognathus ovillus* is found on the head and hairy parts of the lower body and *L. pedalis* occurs on the feet and lower limbs. These are sucking lice which feed on the blood of their host and are blue-black in colour with pointed heads. The biting lice are represented by *Damalina ovis*, which feeds on skin or debris and is brown with a rounded head.

Lice are of limited pathogenic significance but heavy infestations cause marked irritation, restlessness and rubbing with loss of fleece (Fig. 19.1). If sucking lice are involved there may be anaemia and general debility can lead to increased susceptibility to other diseases.

Fig. 19.1
Lice on the face of a
sheep. Heavy louse
infestations may lead
to extensive fleece
loss and loss of
condition.

MITES

The most important mite infection of sheep is *Psoroptes ovis* (Fig. 19.2), which causes sheep scab. This disease was eradicated from Britain in 1952 but was reintroduced in 1973 and complete re-eradication remains to be achieved.

The mites live on the skin surface and pierce the epidermis to feed on lymph. Small pustules develop at the puncture sites

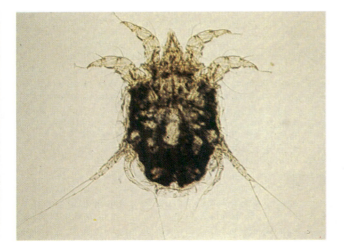

Fig. 19.2
The sheep scab mite,
Psoroptes ovis. Note
the oval body with
long projecting legs;
bell-shaped suckers
on long segmented
pedicels on the first,
second and fourth
pairs of legs indicate
this is a female mite.

and these rupture exuding serum which forms a hard yellow crust. This lifts from the skin together with the wool. There is probably a hypersensitivity reaction to the presence of active mites which causes a marked pruritus. There is extensive loss of fleece and the exposed skin is thickened with raw patches which are often secondarily infected with bacteria (Fig. 19.3).

The lesions observed are the result of a combination of factors: damage caused by the mites during feeding, the host's immune responses to the mites, secondary bacterial infection and self-inflicted trauma in response to the irritation. Loss of condition is rapid and deaths may occur.

Sheep often have pieces of wool stuck between their teeth as a result of nibbling. A "nibble reflex", similar to that elicited in sheep with scrapie may be obtained on rubbing the affected area.

The lesions occur particularly over the shoulders and sides but can spread over the whole body. The mites are found mostly at the edge of the expanding lesion which is characteristically moist. This moist scab is only likely to be seen with psoroptic mange and with no other ectoparasitic infection.

Most clinical cases are seen in winter although in summer the disease still occurs in a milder, much more variable form in which marked irritation may not be a feature.

Three phases of sheep scab are described:

(1) *Active winter scab* – At peak severity this affects up to

Fig. 19.3
Sheep showing extensive loss of fleece, with skin thickening and marked pruritus associated with infection by the sheep scab mite, *Psoroptes ovis.*

three-quarters of the body surface, seen 6–12 weeks after initial infection.

(2) *Active summer scab* – A slowly progressive disease with increasing severity as winter approaches.

(3) *Latent scab* – Recovery following the onset of warmer weather with disappearance of all lesions by mid-summer. Relapse will occur next winter, in the absence of effective treatment.

Psoroptic mange in sheep is notifiable and if the disease is suspected the divisional veterinary officer of the Ministry of Agriculture, Fisheries and Food or Department of Agriculture and Fisheries, Scotland should be informed. In severe active cases with large numbers of mites present, it is possible to actually see the mites at the edges of lesions. Placing suspect material on a dark background (e.g. carbon paper) will render the barely visible light-coloured mites more obvious.

Unless there is known contact with another infected flock microscopic confirmation will be required and scrapings must be taken for the laboratory (Table 19.3). In the case of *Psoroptes* the sample needs to be relatively superficial since the mites live on the skin surface. The sample should be taken from the edge of the lesion after removal of excess wool. A scraping should be placed in a mite-proof glass or plastic container for transmission to the laboratory.

It should be noted that this type of sample may not be the most appropriate for the diagnosis of other skin conditions, such as dermatophilosis. Samples for the investigation of such infections are better collected dry into paper packets or envelopes with representative samples being obtained from different areas of the lesion.

In the laboratory if mites cannot be identified on a direct low power ($\times$ 10) examination, the material is digested in 10% sodium hydroxide and re-examined under higher power. A variety of species of mite may be found in material obtained from sheep and non-parasitic forage mites (*Tyroglyphidae*) are often seen. Occasionally they may be associated with a pruritic reaction, if present in large numbers. Recently, a number of outbreaks of severe pruritus have been recorded in clipped, housed sheep associated with heavy infestations of forage mites.

Table 19.3 The identification of mites in skin scrapings from sheep.

Mite	Identification features
Psoroptes species	Oval body with well-developed, projecting legs. Bell-shaped suckers present on **long three-segmented** pedicels associated with 1st, 2nd and 3rd (male) and 1st, 2nd and 4th (female) legs are diagnostic of this species (see Fig. 19.2)
Chorioptes species	Oval body with long projecting legs. Bell-shaped suckers are present on **short non-segmented** pedicels associated with all legs (male) and 1st, 2nd and 4th legs (female)
Sarcoptes species	Oval body with short legs which do not protrude much beyond the body edge. Suckers are present on long, unsegmented pedicels on legs 1, 2 and 4 (male) and legs 1 and 2 (female), transverse striations present on dorsal surface
Demodex species	Cigar shaped; divided into head, thorax (with four pairs of short, stumpy legs) and an elongated transversely striated body
Trombicula species (Harvest mite)	Red or orange, 0.2–0.4 mm long. Larvae are parasitic on all species (including man). All legs have seven segments. The body is covered in dense hairs. Unlikely to be confused with any of the above species
Tyroglyphidae species (Forage mites)	These are often encountered present as chance contaminants from bedding, food, etc. Occasionally associated with a dermatitis. Distinguished from the pathogenic species by presence of numerous long hairs or bristles, an absence of suckers and, on some species, hooks on legs

Note Infection with *Psoroptes* species or *Sarcoptes* species is notifiable in Britain. If the presence of either is suspected, this should be reported to the Ministry of Agriculture, Fisheries and Food, with which responsibility for final confirmation rests

OTHER PARASITIC MITES

Chorioptes ovis occurs commonly in sheep but is not considered of great economic or pathological importance. The mites are found in the interdigital spaces particularly but can extend up the legs to the knees or hocks. In addition they are found around the scrotum, the brisket and the infraorbital region.

The disease is generally mild. There may be a slight dermatitis and wrinkling of the skin with the development of pustules.

Sarcoptes scabiei var. *ovis* is, like *Psoroptes ovis*, notifiable and is covered by the same legislation, both infections being referred to under the legally defined term "sheep scab".

Sarcoptic mange has not been seen in sheep in Britain for many years. It affects those areas of the body which are devoid of wool and the deeply burrowing mites cause intense irritation with thickening and roughening of the skin. Cure is very difficult to achieve because of the deep-seated nature of the infection in the skin and repeated treatments are usually needed to clear up cases.

Demodex folliculorum var. *ovis* occurs in sheep in Britain but clinical disease is rare and of little significance. The mites live in hair follicles and sebaceous glands and they cause the development of hard scaly areas with intense irritation in a few cases.

FLIES

STRIKE (MYIASIS)

Myiasis is the invasion of living tissues by the larvae of dipteran flies. This condition will be familiar to all dealing with sheep and follows as a result of female blowflies laying eggs, particularly in areas of soiled fleece. The soiling may be the result of scouring, bleeding from wounds (castration, docking, shearing, headfly, tick bites, etc.) or infection may be established in footrot lesions.

Blowfiles are divided into two groups. Primary flies produce larvae which are capable of lacerating skin and producing proteolytic enzymes which digest tissue. Secondary flies are unable to initiate a strike but they are attracted to damaged areas and take advantage of the situation created by the primary flies.

The clinical signs shown by affected sheep include restlessness, reluctance to graze and characteristically atypical posturing with the head inclined towards the affected area and smacking movements of the lips. Close examination will reveal a foul smelling area of moist brown wool with maggots present. Later the wool falls out leaving an irregular wound exuding foul smelling liquid. The larvae at this stage are invading the tissues and only their posterior parts are visible.

Strike occurs during the summer months when as a result of higher temperatures there is a large increase in fly population with an accelerated life cycle. The sheep become more susceptible to fly strike as the fleece gets longer and where there is soiling with faeces. Often wet conditions result in mycotic infection of the fleece which is then followed by blowfly strike.

HEADFLY

Headfly disease in sheep in Britain is associated with a muscid fly, *Hydrotaea irritans*. This species occurs in vast numbers in areas of suitable habitat and is a major problem in certain parts of Britain, particularly the north of England, south-west Scotland and the Scottish borders. Up to 200,000 headfly per hectare have been estimated to be present in areas of woodland, whereas 400 blowflies per hectare would be considered a high level of population.

Although the headfly occurs widely throughout Britain, the disease associated with it appears limited to the areas mentioned. This is likely to be because sheep traditionally kept in these areas are the horned breeds, e.g. Scottish blackface, which are susceptible to damage beginning in the soft tissue at the base of the horns.

Naturally polled breeds, particularly those with wool (rather than hair) covering their heads are much less susceptible although under conditions of severe challenge these too may develop lesions.

Lesions appear with the onset of headfly activity (early June onwards) and only heal when the fly activity ceases as autumn frosts begin.

The lesions vary greatly in severity but in some cases over 70% of the flock may be affected with the loss of large areas of skin from the head. These open wounds may be secondarily infected with bacteria or blowfly larvae. Healing may leave permanent scarring (Fig. 19.4).

The activity of headfly is very dependent on weather conditions. Most of the fly's life is spent roosting in the shelter

Fig. 19.4
Damage to the heads of sheep, particularly horned breeds, during the summer months is usually caused by the activities of the sheep headfly, *Hydrotaea irritans*. The lesions heal when fly activity ceases but the animals may be permanently disfigured.

of trees and individuals only emerge to feed on a few occasions during the summer. On still, warm, humid, overcast days vast numbers of flies will approach sheep to feed on nasal or lacrimal secretions.

The presence of the flies around the sheep's heads causes considerable distress and the efforts of the sheep to avoid the flies results in damage to the head. Once the skin is broken large numbers of flies attack the wound and there is a rapid extension of the lesion. Headfly have been incriminated in the spread of New Forest disease and summer mastitis, probably acting simply as mechanical carriers.

KEDS

Keds are parasitic flies which have evolved a close relationship with their host and have lost their wings, remaining permanently on the sheep. *Melophagus ovinus* (Fig. 19.5) is of limited pathological significance although heavy infestations can cause anaemia. Keds are often present together with lice and the clinical signs associated with the two infections are similar (Fig. 19.6).

Fig. 19.5
The sheep ked,
Melophagus ovinus.
This wingless fly is
readily controlled by
dipping, using
organophosphorous
insecticides.

Fig. 19.6
Infestation with lice
and keds leads to
extensive fleece loss
and reduced
resistance to cold
stress.

OTHER FLIES

In contrast to the case in cattle, particularly dairy cattle where the economics of fly worry on milk yield have been studied in some depth, little or no work has been done on the effects of fly worry on sheep.

In cattle, reduced growth rates and lowered milk yields are the result of disturbed grazing activity and it is likely that a similar situation prevails in sheep although at an economically less significant level.

In addition to disturbed grazing there may be skin reactions and irritation at the sites of bites (bare, unprotected areas) and in some countries (not UK) important diseases of sheep are transmitted by biting flies. The bites of some of the larger horseflies bleed for some time after the wound is made and the blood may attract other species, such as headflies or blowflies, leading to further damage.

CONTROL OF ECTOPARASITE INFECTION

The most common method of sheep ectoparasite control is the use of parasiticides to kill the parasites on the host. Attention should also be given to factors which adversely affect the parasites' environment, either on the host (e.g. shearing) or off the host (e.g. pasture management).

Various methods have been developed for applying parasiticides to sheep. Those used in Britain include dipping baths, showers, spray races and, more recently, pour-ons.

The plunge dipping bath is the surest way to achieve thorough wetting and spread of the chemical over the whole animal and is the only method approved for the control of sheep scab. The sheep should remain in the bath long enough to allow saturation of the fleece (one minute is legally required for scab control) (Fig. 19.7).

While in the bath the sheep should be kept moving to dislodge air pockets in the fleece and allow penetration of the parasiticide. They should have their heads immersed twice. Dipping baths should be accurately calibrated and permanent marks made on the side of the bath or on a dip stick. The

Fig. 19.7
Sheep which are being dipped should remain in the bath for one minute; while in the bath they should have their heads completely immersed twice.

exact volume of sheep dip recommended by the manufacturer should be added to clean water in the bath to produce the "dip wash". As the sheep pass through the dipping bath they remove dip wash in the fleece; a draining pen (ideally two) should be provided for the sheep to stand in while the excess dip wash drains back into the bath.

With most sheep dips the parasiticide is preferentially removed on to the fleece, lowering the concentration of chemical in the dipping bath. This is compensated for by using a higher replenishment concentration of chemical when the bath is "topped up" or by allowing a higher concentration of chemical to flow continuously into the bath during dipping.

Showers and spray races provide a faster means for the application of parasiticides to sheep than dipping but do not provide such thorough coverage of the whole animal and are therefore not approved for scab treatment and control. The equipment should be used according to the manufacturer's directions and should be checked before and during use to ensure that spray nozzles are not blocked.

With the shower, a pump delivers the parasiticide through nozzles in a rotating boom and through nozzles on the floor on to the sheep in an enclosed pen. With the spray race the parasiticide is delivered through a series of nozzles situated along a tunnel through which the sheep pass.

The pour-on method of application uses a special formulation of insecticide which, when applied to a small area on the back, spreads over the skin surface of the animal. Pour-ons are a relatively new development and so far are indicated only for the control of body lice.

Maggot fly may be controlled by dipping, showering or spraying using any one of a number of effective larvacidal products belonging to the organophosphorous group of compounds. These include coumaphos, chlorfenvinphos, diazinon, carbophenothion, chlorpyrifos and dioxathion.

When used in a dipping bath these products will normally give a complete season's protection against fly strike. Proper attention should be given to helminth control as sheep which are dirty and scouring from parasitic gastroenteritis are more attractive to the maggot fly. It is good practice to dock lambs' tails early in life and clip away any dirty wool at regular intervals. Prophylactic treatment is usually carried out after shearing when ideally at least three weeks' growth of wool should be present to ensure good retention of the insecticide.

Lice and keds are very susceptible to insecticidal treatments. They spend their entire life cycle on the host so the organophosphorous compounds mentioned above will eradicate lice in one dipping and provide about five months' protection against reinfestation. Treatment against lice and keds is usually carried out in the autumn or in February and March when the infestation becomes apparent.

Three acaricides, gamma-hexachlorocyclohexane, diazinon and propetamphos, are ministry-approved for sheep scab control in Britain. Each will eradicate sheep scab in one dipping and provide at least four weeks' protection against reinfestation. At the beginning of the present campaign to eradicate sheep scab animals were dipped in the late autumn but in recent years summer dipping has been required.

Organophosphorous compounds are commonly used for tick control, including coumaphos, diazinon, dioxathion, chlorpyrifos and chlorfenvinphos. Sheep are treated just before the ticks start to feed in the autumn or spring. The products used impart a variable period of protection lasting three or more weeks. If the tick season is prolonged more than one dipping my be required.

Dipping is aimed at reducing the number of ticks on the pasture over a period of years. Pasture improvement should also be considered as this will reduce the thick matt undergrowth which provides the high humidity essential for tick survival off the host. Unfortunately, pasture improvement tends to be most difficult and expensive in those areas where ticks are a problem. Nevertheless, the additional benefits of increased production from the pasture may make it worthwhile.

The control of headfly damage presents particular problems and so far no totally effective practical control system has been developed. Dips (including dieldrin) are of little or no value and locally applied insecticides or repellents give at best only partial control. Headcaps give fairly good control although they are time consuming to apply. The use of slow-release devices consisting of a plastic base from which an insecticide or repellent is released over a period of months has promise and is the subject of current investigation.

RESISTANCE PROBLEMS

Fortunately, ectoparasites which have become resistant to compounds are not a problem in Britain. The only documented case is of a strain of lice in Westmoreland in 1965 which was resistant to gamma-hexachlorocyclohexane and also to dieldrin. The strain was controlled by organophosphorous compounds. No other cases of resistance have been recorded in Britain.

ACKNOWLEDGEMENTS

The colour figures, with the exception of Fig. 19.4, are used by courtesy of the Wellcome Foundation.

CHAPTER 20

Non-parasitic Skin Diseases of Sheep

GEORGE B. B. MITCHELL

INTRODUCTION

The maintenance of a healthy skin is extremely important for sheep of all ages. It provides not only the first line of defence against invading microorganisms but also plays a vital role in other body functions, e.g. temperature regulation and fluid/electrolyte balance. Any breach of this barrier will affect one or all of these functions and may also lead to systemic illness (Table 20.1).

HEREDITARY/CONGENITAL CONDITIONS

RED FOOT

Red foot occurs in the Scottish blackface and its crosses, on hill ground within the first few weeks of life.

Table 20.1 Non-parasitic skin diseases of sheep

Hereditary/congenital	Red foot
Viral	Border disease
	Contagious pustular dermatitis
	Foot-and-mouth disease
Bacterial	Actinobacillosis
	Clostridial infection of wounds
	Staphylococcal folliculitis
	Staphylococcal dermatitis
	Scald
Fungal	Mycotic dermatitis
	Ringworm
Miscellaneous	Photosensitization
	Fleece rot
	Wool slip
	Skin tumours
	Sunburn

Clinical signs

Progressive lameness and recumbency (Fig. 20.1). Affected lambs may walk on their knees and be unable to suck. Death caused by starvation and secondary infection is common.

Fig. 20.1
Red foot in a
neonatal blackface
lamb.

Pathology

Loss of hoof horn often accompanied by ulceration of the oral mucous membranes, cornea, and occasionally the skin of the ears and limbs. The basic lesion appears to be inadequate attachment of the stratified squamous epithelium to the underlying corium. Some authors consider the disease to be related to epithelogenesis imperfecta in cattle or epidermolysis bullosa of children. It is thought to have a hereditary component, the exact nature of which remains obscure.

Confirmation of diagnosis

Clinical signs, incidence and gross pathology are diagnostic.

Treatment and prevention

No treatment is possible, affected lambs should be euthanized. If particular sires are incriminated, these should be culled.

VIRAL DISEASES

BORDER DISEASE (HAIRY SHAKERS, CONGENITAL TREMBLES)

This disease, which occurs widely in the UK, affects lambs in utero as a result of a pestivirus infection of pregnant ewes. Although primarily a nervous disease, pathological changes also occur in the skin. The disease was fully described by Barlow (1987) and in Chapter 11.

Clinical signs

Abortion or birth of diseased live lambs. Affected lambs have a characteristically hairy coat which may be pigmented and contains long fine "halo" hairs often over the neck region. A severe muscle tremor is common, with erratic gait and incoordination.

Pathology

Hypomyelinogenesis is evident in brain and spinal cord. The skin abnormalities are related to the action of the virus on foetal ectoderm resulting in hypertrophy of the primary hair follicles with medullation and a relative decrease in the numbers of secondary follicles.

Diagnosis

Clinical signs specific to this disease confirmed by neuropathology and/or isolation of the causal pestivirus from tissues of affected lambs. Serology of ewes may also be helpful where abortions are occurring.

Treatment and control

No treatment is possible for affected lambs. The disease may be controlled by segregation and disposal of affected ewes and their lambs. If the disease is widespread throughout the flock then control measures should be aimed at exposing susceptible ewes to infection and thereby immunizing them, by mixing them with surviving lambs, 4–6 weeks before tupping. Affected lambs should then be slaughtered before ewes become pregnant.

CONTAGIOUS PUSTULAR DERMATITIS (ORF, CONTAGIOUS ECTHYMA, SCABBY MOUTH)

Orf is a well-recognized disease of sheep caused by a *Parapox* species virus, occurring commonly on the commissures of mouth, lips, muzzle (Fig. 20.2) and occasionally on the feet and genitalia of young lambs in spring and summer. Lesions may also occur on teats and udder of ewes when the condition can be particularly troublesome.

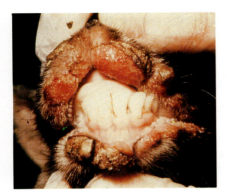

Fig. 20.2
Severe orf affecting skin of lips and mouth.
(Courtesy of Dr G. R. Scott)

Clinical signs and pathology

The initial lesion consists of a number of red papules within which vesicles develop, rupture and a thick scab is formed. Proliferative changes may then occur resulting in papillomatous lesions. Secondary bacterial infection is common and in ewes mastitis may occur. Difficulty in sucking may cause weight restriction in lambs and lesions on the coronary band may result in lameness.

Confirmation of diagnosis

Sites and lesions tend to be pathognomonic; confirmation is by demonstration of viral particles by electron microscopy on scabs or proliferative lesions.

Treatment and prevention

The disease spreads rapidly by contact with infected animals and once established antibiotic treatment will only limit secondary infection, while limiting spread of the virus by isolation of affected animals is frequently unsuccessful. Two live vaccines are currently available for prevention in ewes and lambs. The vaccines are normally applied to the skin of the inside of the thigh six weeks before lambing. There is no evidence of colostral protection, hence on problem farms young lambs will also require vaccination soon after birth. Protection of lambs by vaccination tends to be variable depending on the weight of challenge and the stocking rate.

FOOT-AND-MOUTH DISEASE

The vesicular lesion of this notifiable highly contagious disease which may infect sheep may be confused with early lesions of orf, although FMD in sheep is characterized by lameness caused by interdigital lesions in the early stages. If FMD is suspected confirmation will be undertaken by MAFF who should be informed immediately.

BACTERIAL DISEASES

ACTINOBACILLOSIS (CRUELS, KING'S EVIL)

Sporadic outbreaks of actinobacillosis, characterized by thickening of the skin of the head with multiple subcutaneous abscesses in the lymphatic chain of the head and neck region (Fig. 20.3), have been recorded, particularly in adult rams, associated with *Actinobacillus lignieresi*. The organism is thought to gain access by infection of wounds or abrasions. Treatment with antibiotics (e.g. streptomycin injection) is normally effective if carried out in the early stages.

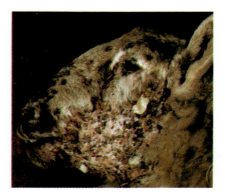

Fig. 20.3
Actinobacillosis. Ewe showing multiple subcutaneous abscesses on face. (Courtesy of Dr K. A. Linklater)

CLOSTRIDIAL INFECTION OF WOUNDS (MALIGNANT OEDEMA, BIG HEAD OF RAMS)

Acute rapidly fatal infections in all ages of sheep are associated with contamination of wounds, particularly deep puncture wounds by a variety of *Clostridium* species including *C. chauvoei, C. oedematiens, C. perfringens, C. septicum,* and *C. sordellii* species.

Clinical signs and pathology

Swelling of affected area initially hot, becoming cold, often with crepitus, pain/stiffness, high fever and death within 48 hours. Swelling with oedema of the head may occur in rams which have been fighting, rapidly causing death. The lesion is usually dark red with subcutaneous oedema, gas formation, accumulation of bloodstained fluid and cellulitis and characteristic if the animal is seen alive or shortly after death.

Confirmation of diagnosis

This can be difficult due to rapid post-mortem autolysis of affected animals obscuring the primary site of infection. Isolation by anaerobic culture may be successful if the sheep is freshly dead. A rapid, specific diagnosis will require making smears of affected areas for fluorescent antibody techniques (FAT) using specific antisera.

Treatment and prevention

If detected early enough treatment with large doses of crystalline penicillin may be life-saving. Attention to hygiene, particularly with regard to injection techniques, sterilization of needles, hygiene at lambing, use of disinfectants and prompt attention to shearing/docking wounds will reduce the incidence. Numerous, effective clostridial vaccines are available commercially.

STAPHYLOCCAL FOLLICULITIS (PLUKEY LAMBS)

A benign condition of young lambs, especially those kept indoors which may also affect milking ewes (mammary impetigo).

Clinical signs and pathology

This condition is characteristically associated with small pustules around the lips, muzzle, nostrils (Fig. 20.4) or perineum which rapidly become encrusted, pitted when the scab is removed, and are non-granulomatous (cf. orf). Histopathologically the lesion is a pyogenic folliculitis with ulceration of the epidermis.

Confirmation of diagnosis

Characteristic lesions from which coagulase-positive β-haemolytic *Staphylococcus aureus* can readily be isolated.

Treatment and control

No treatment is necessary but it is important to differentiate this condition from orf and staphylococcal dermatitis (below).

Fig. 20.4
Staphylococcal folliculitis. Lesions on nares of lamb (arrow). (Courtesy of Dr G. R. Scott)

STAPHYLOCOCCAL DERMATITIS (FACIAL ECZEMA, PERIORBITAL ECZEMA, EYE SCAB)

A severe suppurative condition affecting the face, limbs and occasionally vulva of ewes and prepuce of rams.

Clinical signs and pathology

All ewes may be affected, but often trough-fed ewes succumb before lambing with suppurative ulceration of the skin around the eyes (Fig. 20.5), ears and base of the horns, scab formation and local alopecia. Lower limb lesions may also occur especially around the coronet. Complete resolution may take at least six weeks. Histopathology reveals abscessation in the dermis with exudation of pus from overlying necrotic epidermis; accumulation of mononuclear cells and ultimately necrosis of subcutaneous tissues.

Confirmation of diagnosis

Clinical assessment of lesions and isolation of the causal haemolytic *Staphylococcus aureus*. The condition should be differentiated from proliferative orf lesions and the necrotic lesions of photosensitization which affect only unpigmented areas of skin.

Fig. 20.5
Staphylococcal dermatitis. Periorbital and facial lesions on ewe. (Courtesy of Mr D. Gray)

Treatment and control

Early antibiotic treatment both local and parenteral in severe cases is indicated. Affected areas should be flushed with sterile isotonic saline and necrotic debris removed. Control measures should be aimed at reducing the risk of skin trauma, i.e. removal of thistles from grazing and providing adequate trough space inside to reduce aggression.

SCALD (SCAD, BENIGN FOOTROT)

Clinical signs and pathology

Lameness, especially in young sheep on lush pasture, under warm moist conditions. The interdigital skin becomes inflamed and painful (Fig. 20.6). There may be some separation of soft horn, but suppuration is not a feature, the disease is not normally progressive and the typical "footrot smell" is absent. A number of workers suggest that it is frequently difficult to distinguish scad from early lesions of true footrot either on clinical or pathological grounds as the ultimate pathology will be dependent on the strain of *B. nodosus* involved.

Fig. 20.6
Typical interdigital lesions of scad. (Courtesy of Dr K. A. Linklater)

Confirmation of diagnosis

Demonstration of anaerobic *Bacteroides nodosus* (Gram-negative rods with swollen ends) in Gram-stained films of affected skin. *Fusibacterium necrophorum*, which facilitates entry of other anaerobes by destruction of leucocytes, may also be present.

Treatment and control

Topical application of antibiotic aerosol is normally effective in uncomplicated cases. Control measures for footrot, i.e. attention to foot care, particularly regular examination of feet, paring of overgrown horn and frequent passage through foot baths will reduce the incidence. Commercially available zinc sulphate solutions may prove more useful that the more traditional noxious formaldehyde.

FUNGAL DISEASES

MYCOTIC DERMATITIS (ACTINOMYCOTIC DERMATITIS, DERMATOPHILOSIS, LUMPY WOOL, STRAWBERRY FOOTROT)

Mycotic dermatitis, commonly known as "lumpy wool" is a common condition seen in sheep of all ages, caused by infection with *Dermatophilus congolensis*, strictly speaking an actinomycete (higher bacterium) and not a fungus as the name suggests. Economic importance of the disease lies in the downgrading of affected fleeces and the condition must be distinguished from sheep scab caused by the mange mite *Psoroptes ovis* and ringworm infection.

Clinical signs and pathology

The disease is essentially an exudative dermatitis affecting particularly the skin of the ears and face in lambs and the woolly areas of the back and flanks in adult sheep (Fig. 20.7). In rams the skin of the scrotum may be affected. The disease progresses from hyperaemia with exudation to crust and scab formation, associated with invasion of the epidermis by branching filamentous forms of *D. congolensis*. In severe cases wool loss and fleece damage may occur. Penetration of the epidermis is facilitated by prolonged wetting of the fleece during periods of wet weather. When the skin immediately above the coronet is affected the condition is commonly termed "strawberry footrot" due to the appearance of proliferative lesions with bleeding points evident on removal of the tenacious scabs.

Confirmation of diagnosis

A tentative diagnosis on clinical grounds may be easily confirmed by Giemsa-stained preparations of moistened, macerated scab material in which coccal and filamentous forms of *D. congolensis* may be readily demonstrated.

Treatment and control

Most cases will heal spontaneously over a period of weeks, recovery will be accelerated by application of a proprietary dusting powder containing 1% potassium aluminium sulphate (alum) in the autumn and will respond to injection of long-acting tetracycline, penicillin or streptomycin. In flocks with a recurring problem summer and autumn/winter dips contain-

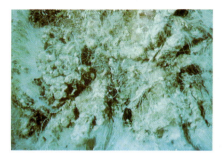

Fig. 20.7
Mycotic dermatitis. Lesions on the back of a ewe.
(Courtesy of Edinburgh VI Centre)

ing either 0.5% zinc sulphate or 1% alum should be used to control infection.

In cases where secondary bacterial infection has occurred parenteral or topical antibiotic treatment is essential.

RINGWORM

Ringworm, a fungal disease seen commonly in young calves, occasionally occurs in sheep due to invasion of the skin by *Trichophyton verrucosum*.

Clinical signs and pathology

Areas commonly affected include the face, ears and back and occasionally the legs and tailhead. The lesions are first seen as firm raised plaques attached to the overlying wool, which then becomes detached to reveal circular raised crusts with local thickening of the skin (Fig. 20.8). The degree of irritation caused tends to be variable but severe pruritus is not common. Histopathologically thickening of the stratum spinosum with hyperkeratosis and proliferative dermatitis has been described.

Fig. 20.8
Ringworm lesions on back and flanks of affected ewe. (Courtesy of Dr Q. McKellar)

Confirmation of diagnosis

Microscopic examination of skin scrapings and affected hairs in potassium hydroxide will reveal fungal spores and/or hyphae and the fungus may be cultured using selective media containing antibiotics, e.g. Oxoid Dermasel Agar.

Treatment and prevention

Affected sheep will recover without treatment but in severe cases and to limit spread of the disease, segregation of affected sheep and treatment with a fungicide either topical, e.g. natamycin (Mycophyt; Mycofarm) or oral, e.g. griseofulvin (Grisovin; Coopers Pitman-Moore), is recommended. Thorough cleaning and disinfection of buildings contaminated by other livestock, e.g. calves, to which sheep have access should prevent reinfection.

MISCELLANEOUS CONDITIONS

PHOTOSENSITIZATION (YELLOWSES, PLOCHTEACHT, SAUT, ALVELD [ELF-FIRE])

This condition occurs because of the presence of photodynamic substance(s) in the skin capable of causing severe dermatitis in the presence of sunlight. Such agents release energy obtained from light in hyperoxidative processes harmful to skin. Photosensitization, as described in Great Britain, may be either primary, i.e. as a result of ingestion of a photodynamic agent (e.g. hypericin in *Hypericum perforatum* [St John's wort]), or by administration of a photosensitizing drug, e.g. phenothiazine; or secondary (indirect or hepatogenous) due to impairment of liver function resulting in failure to denature chlorophyll and build-up of the photodynamic agent phylloerythrin in tissues. Examples of the latter include the ingestion of *Narthrecium ossifragum* (bog asphodel) and rape poisoning which have been asssociated with photosensitization in Scotland and England.

Fig. 20.9
Photosensitization.
Early lesions on back
of ewe. (Courtesy of
Edinburgh VI Centre)

Clinical signs and pathology

In disease outbreaks involving bog asphodel young lambs grazing wet hill pastures, where the plant flourishes, are affected. The lesions (Figs 20.9 and 20.10) occur on the ears, face, muzzle, back, fore legs and scrotum or perineum. Swelling and oedema of unpigmented skin is rapidly followed by yellowish crusting, exudation and finally sloughing of affected tissue giving lambs a characteristic "cropped" appearance when the ears are involved. Jaundice may also rarely occur, but hepatic degeneration is demonstrable histopathologically.

Fig. 20.10
Photosensitization associated with bog asphodel showing typical yellowish crusting of the skin and "cropped appearance" following sloughing of affected ear. (Courtesy of Perth VI Centre)

Confirmation of diagnosis

A confident diagnosis may be made on the basis of typical skin lesions together with access to pasture known to contain St John's wort or bog asphodel or recent treatment with a photosensitizing drug. Elevated serum levels of phylloerythrin and, in the case of hepatogenous disease, liver enzymes would confirm the diagnosis.

Treatment and control

Corticosteroid injection has been used prophylactically on problem farms in Perthshire with equivocal results. Norwegian workers who produced the disease experimentally by dosing lambs with a saponin-containing extract of bog asphodel also demonstrated variability in resistance to photosensitization dependent on haemoglobin type, suggesting that genetic selection of resistant sheep may be possible. If practicable housing of affected sheep to preclude exposure to sunlight and grazing overnight will be beneficial.

FLEECE ROT (CANARY STAIN)

This condition, characterized by pigmentation of the fleece following periods of prolonged wetting is a major problem in Australia as a predisposing factor in blowfly strike. Chemical changes which occur in the fleece result in breakdown of wool wax associated with a number of pigment-producing bacteria, including *Pseudomonas aeruginosa*, may lead to downgrading of the fleece. The condition has been produced experimentally by disruption of the sebaceous layer of the skin with petroleum solvent.

During the wet summer of 1985 the condition was observed in a number of flocks in eastern Scotland and could be transferred artificially from sheep to sheep using portions of affected fleece.

Clinical signs and pathology

Superficial dermatitis with seropurulent exudation, matting and frequently pigmentation of the wool.

Confirmation of diagnosis

Typical appearance of the fleece and isolation of pigment-producing organisms including *Pseudomonas aeruginosa*. The possibility of mycotic dermatitis due to *Dermatophilus congolensis* should also be explored at an early stage.

Treatment and control

As for mycotic dermatitis. Use of certain antibacterial skin preparations may also be of value in controlling *Pseudomonas* species. Vaccination against fleece rot using preparations derived from *Pseudomonas aeruginosa* has reduced the incidence of both fleece rot and blowfly strike in Australia.

WOOL SLIP (ALOPECIA)

This condition has been described in ewes following winter shearing. Although not associated with severe signs of illness it is a common cause of concern for the flock owner as it is unsightly, and in ewes in poor condition during periods of cold weather may result in a welfare problem. The condition has been observed in ewes with low serum copper values undergoing cold stress and it has been suggested that elevated plasma cortisol levels may be involved.

Clinical signs and pathology

Wool loss and alopecia with bald patches developing over the hindquarters, back and neck in most cases. Wool may be easily plucked from affected areas, but underlying skin appears normal and pruritus does not occur. Wool loss is progressive, often commencing several weeks after winter shearing in housed ewes.

Confirmation of diagnosis

The condition can be diagnosed on clinical grounds having
ruled out other causes of alopecia on the absence of gross skin
pathology.

Treatment and control

No treatment is possible, therefore control measures based on
minimizing periods of stress by shearing earlier or shearing
and housing at the same time and by offering a better quality
ration prior to housing are recommended.

SKIN TUMOURS

This type of tumour is uncommon in sheep in the UK although
sporadic cases have been described including papillomata,
neurofibromas and malignant melanomas. The latter occurs in
pigmented areas of skin especially in the Suffolk breed and
is extremely malignant with rapid, widespread dissemination
of tumour cells. In valuable animals surgical removal of benign
lesions may be advisable in some cases.

SUNBURN

The harmful effects of ultraviolet radiation from direct sunlight
in shorn sheep should not be forgotten as a potential cause
of skin damage, particularly on grazing where shade is not
available. In ewes encrustment of non-pigmented skin with
ultimately necrosis of the epidermis, upper dermis and superficial sebaceous glands may occur.

Treatment and control

Housing of affected sheep and topical application of emollients
to affected areas is recommended. In severe cases treatment
of secondary bacterial dermatitis with antibiotics will be
necessary.

REFERENCES AND FURTHER READING

Barlow, R. M. (1987). *In Practice* **9**, 3.
Lloyd, D. H. (1985). *British Veterinary Journal* **141**, 463.
Martin, W. (1983). *Diseases of Sheep*. Blackwell Scientific Publications, Oxford.
Morgan, K. L., Brown, P. J. Wright, A. I., Steele, F. C. & Baker, A. S. (1986). *Veterinary Record* **119**, 621.

CHAPTER 21

Skin Diseases in Goats

PETER JACKSON

INTRODUCTION

Although the incidence of skin disease in goats is quite low, individual cases may cause considerable problems to both owner and veterinary surgeon. The owner may suffer both anxiety and economic loss. Show appearances may have to be cancelled, breeding plans halted and much time and expense may have to be devoted to treatment To the veterinarian caprine skin disease presents a challenge both in terms of diagnosis and treatment. The value of individual goats may be less than the cost of effective diagnosis and treatment. In recent years goat numbers have increased and there has also been an increase in the movement of animals to shows and to stud. As a result of this, the risk of spread of contagious diseases, including some skin conditions, has undoubtedly also increased.

For the treatment of any disease to be effective it must be preceded by an accurate diagnosis and this is especially important in cases of caprine skin disease. Ideally treatment should not commence until diagnosis is complete. In practice the veterinarian is often under pressure to commence treatment at once if only to allay distressing symptoms. Before treatment is applied it is important to ensure that any samples required to confirm the diagnosis have been taken and preserved.

The clinical signs of skin disease in goats vary greatly. The owner's attention may be attracted by hair loss, changes in skin colour or by the presence of pruritus. In some conditions such as chorioptic mange, the mild signs of skin disease may pass unnoticed, while in other conditions such as sarcoptic mange, severe and debilitating pruritus may dominate the clinical appearance of the patient. In most cases, skin disease is caused by specific pathogens or by recognized chemical or physical agents (Table 21.1). Poor skin condition and hair growth may be just one aspect of debilitating diseases such as intestinal parasitism.

DIAGNOSIS OF SKIN DISEASE

Diagnosis may be approached in the following stages: case history; clinical examination; special examination of the skin; and collection of samples for clinical pathology.

CASE HISTORY

Adequate time must be allowed for taking and recording a complete and comprehensive case history. Sufficient time is seldom available for this during a normal brief surgery consultation if the case history is to be fully explored. The case history may help to identify the possible source of the skin disease, its time of onset and the main features which have been observed by the owner.

Table 21.1 Causes of caprine skin disease.

Parasites – mange mites, lice, fleas, ticks
Fungi – ringworm
Bacteria – staphylococci, nocardia, dermatophilus, C. *pseudotuberculosis*
Viruses – orf, papillomatosis, scrapie
Allergy
Auto-immune disease – pemphigus foliaceous
Neoplasia – melanoma, haemangioma
Physical and chemical trauma

The main points to be noted during history taking are listed in Table 21.2.

It is essential that every aspect of the case history be carefully pursued and all possible leads followed up. Owners can easily forget vital pieces of information especially if they feel inhibited by lack of time. One area where errors can occur is in regard to movement. The owner may insist that their goat has definitely had no contact with other animals but questioning may reveal that some brief contact with another goat may in fact have occurred.

CLINICAL EXAMINATION

A detailed and thorough clinical examination must precede the special examination of the skin to detect evidence of intercurrent disease which might either have resulted from or caused the skin lesions. Before handling the animal it is often helpful to observe it unobtrusively for signs of nibbling at or rubbing the skin. When seen in its own environment further evidence of pruritus and self-inflicted damage may be observed in the form of a well-rubbed wall or small piles of dislodged hair.

SPECIAL EXAMINATION OF THE SKIN

The entire skin surface of the patient should be examined to determine the nature and distribution of lesions. Initially the skin may be observed from a distance of a few feet to locate areas of abnormality which will receive special attention when

Table 21.2 Main points to be noted when recording a case history.

Date when symptoms first appeared
Symptoms observed by the owner
Contact with other goats
Spread within the herd
Previous health record of affected goat(s)
Other disease problems within the herd past and present
Response to treatment (including home remedies) so far
Details of management including feeding, worming, etc.

the skin is more closely examined. Visual examination is followed by manual examination during which the veterinarian's hands should run over the entire skin surface to identify by touch any lesions in the skin which are not readily visible.

In order to avoid missing any area of the body surface a regular plan of examination should be adopted. Starting with the head and neck observations continue over the trunk and perineal regions and conclude with the legs and feet. During examination of the head special attention should be paid to the periorbital area and the inner and outer surfaces of the pinnae. The mouth and especially the mucocutaneous junction of the lips should also receive attention.

During examination of the trunk, the axillae, udder and inguinal regions – common sites of skin disease – should be carefully inspected. These areas may be more easily seen if the goat is gently rolled on to its side. While in this position the legs and feet may also be readily observed. The consistency of the horny parts of the feet, the interdigital areas and the skin covering the limb joints should all be the subject of special scrutiny.

Areas of abnormality should be examined in even greater detail with the aid of a hand lens and compared with areas of the body in which no abnormality has been detected. The elasticity of the skin, its temperature, thickness, colour and consistency should be noted and the response of the animal to palpation of affected areas should also be noted. The hairs including their follicles should also be the subject of careful scrutiny.

Records should be made of the lesion distribution, most easily recorded by means of sketches which can be amended at subsequent examinations, and the nature of any lesions (Table 21.3).

COLLECTION OF SAMPLES

It may be possible to arrive at a diagnosis at the time of clinical examination, but in long-standing cases laboratory help may be required. Many of the necessary tests are within the scope of a good practice laboratory but others require specialist help. In the case of histological or immunological

Table 21.3 Recording the nature of lesions.

Size, depth and number of lesions
Skin colour, elasticity and odour
Consistency and temperature of skin
Response to palpation of lesions
Hair loss, breakage and follicular attachment
Classification of lesions
Abnormal quantities of secretions
Secondary self-inflicted damage

studies it is always advisable to discuss the collection and preservation of samples with the pathologist before they are taken. Samples collected or fixed incorrectly are generally valueless. Well-collected samples examined by an experienced pathologist will often be invaluable in either proving or refuting a tentative diagnosis. The following samples may be found useful.

Blood sample

A sample for red and white blood cell counts is taken into an EDTA container from the jugular vein. Evidence of anaemia may be found in cases of heavy infestation of the skin by blood-sucking parasites. Neutrophilia may be seen in some cases of bacterial skin infection while eosinophilia may occur in both allergic skin disease or parasitic infestations. Such findings must always be treated with caution since a wide range of normal blood parameters is found in healthy goats. Plasma or serum samples may be taken for biochemical or trace element assay.

Hair sample

Examination of individual hairs microscopically is especially useful in the diagnosis of ringworm. Hairs should be plucked with tweezers from the edge of active lesions and, in some cases, culture for periods of up to three months may be necessary to confirm a diagnosis of ringworm; in cases of doubt treatment should be commenced on suspicion.

Skin swab

Whenever bacterial infection of the skin is suspected a swab should be taken for culture and sensitivity testing. If delay in reaching the laboratory is anticipated the swab should be placed in transport medium. Active lesions near scaly or scabby areas should be selected and care must be taken to avoid contamination of the swab. The skin has a small normal bacterial population in the goat but the culture of a profuse growth of staphylococcus in pure culture from a diseased skin is usually a significant finding.

Skin scraping

Examination of skin scrapings is essential in the diagnosis of certain types of mange. In long-standing cases mites are often very few in number and extremely difficult to find and their absence from a skin scraping does not negate a diagnosis of mange. A number of active lesions are selected and scrapings taken from each. The skin is scraped using a clean scalpel blade until capillary bleeding is seen. To ensure that scrapings are not lost the scalpel blade may be coated with Vaseline. The scrapings should be collected in a wide-mouthed glass tube, covered with potassium hydroxide and warmed over- night in a water bath before being centrifuged and examined microscopically.

Skin biopsy

Histological examination of the skin is one of the most useful aids to diagnosis but to be of value samples must be taken and fixed with care. Small whole thickness strips of skin 25 mm × 5 mm are taken under local anaesthesia. Strict asepsis must be employed and most pathologists prefer three biopsies from normal, abnormal and marginal areas, respectively. After removal the skin strips should be pinned out on a wax block and fixed in formol saline (Fig. 21.1).

Fig. 21.1
Skin biopsy pinned
on to wax and
immersed in formol
saline.

Samples for electron microscopy

Examination of skin samples for the presence of pox virus has been found most useful in the diagnosis of orf. If electron microscopy is available locally, fresh samples may be submitted but otherwise samples may be preserved in buffered glutaraldehyde. Serial samples may prove valuable since the virus may be present in certain skin layers for short periods during infection.

Samples for immunology

In cases in which autoimmune disease is suspected, skin biopsies are taken as described above and either submitted fresh for cutting cryostat sections or preserved in buffered formol saline. The presence of autoantibodies in the skin is demonstrated by direct immunofluorescence.

TREATMENT

The need to delay treatment whenever possible until a tentative diagnosis has been confirmed has already been stressed. If severe pruritus is present the animal may be afforded some relief by local application of corticosteroid cream. Severe self-inflicted damage by biting, rubbing or scratching is quite frequently seen and must be actively prevented whenever possible. Biting can be prevented by fixing an Elizabethan collar or plastic bucket from which the base has been removed to the goat's neck collar. Moving the animal to a new pen and taking it for a walk immediately after the application of skin dressings may have a useful "psychological" effect in preventing further damage. Specific treatment for individual skin conditions is discussed below. Pruritic skin lesions on the trunk may be protected from scratching action by the hooves of the hindlegs by applying a lightweight but strong linen coat to the patient.

SPECIFIC SKIN DISEASES

Only the most important conditions can be discussed in this article.

Parasitic skin disease

Skin disease caused by sarcoptes, chorioptes, psoroptes and demodex mites has been described in goats.

Sarcoptic mange

Undoubtedly the most unpleasant and difficult to treat of all the mange infestations, the incidence of sarcoptic mange in Britain appears to be increasing. In affected animals lesions often first appear around the eyes and ears (Fig. 21.2) but the neck, withers, axillae, groin, udder and perineum soon become involved.

Close examination of affected areas shows severe crusting of the skin with the development of deep fissures and areas of weeping eczema. Self-inflicted damage and intense pruritus are common features together with general debility.

Although the condition is contagious, spread does not normally involve all animals in the herd. The reason for the apparent resistance of some animals is not clear and there is no evidence of immunosuppression in affected animals. Firm diagnosis is based upon isolation of mites in deep skin scrapings or finding them in skin biopsy. Early cases may respond well to local applications of benzyl benzoate, gamma-benzene hexachloride or sulphur soap but in advanced cases their penetration of the grossly thickened skin may be poor. Organophosphorous compounds may be efficacious but toxicity may follow their prolonged use. Treatment with all the above compounds is both tedious and time-consuming. Recently ivermectin (Ivomec; MSD Agvet) has been found

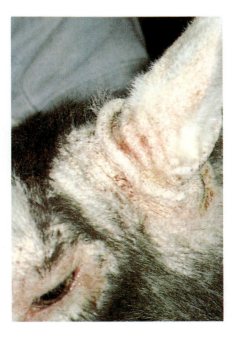

Fig. 21.2
Sarcoptic mange. Lesions on the outer surface of the ear.

most effective, but since it is not licensed for use in goats in Britain it must be used with care.

Chorioptic mange

Lesions of this condition are usually confined to the lower parts of the leg and crusty lesions may be found behind the fetlock joints of all four limbs (Fig. 21.3).

Occasionally signs of pruritus are seen but mostly the condition, which is quite widespread among the goat population, is symptomless. The surface living mite is readily killed by applications of parasiticide, such as gamma-benzene hexachloride, but does not appear to be affected by ivermectin.

Demodectic mange

Less common than either sarcoptic or chorioptic mange, this condition is characterized by the presence of small, well circumscribed skin nodules 1–2 cm in diameter from which large numbers of demodex mites may be expressed (Fig. 21.4). Hair loss and pruritus are not normally seen. Rotenone (Demodectic Mange Dressing; Coopers Pitman-Moore), diluted with three parts of surgical spirit, should be either instilled into evacuated pustules or applied to one-quarter of the body at a time. Amitraz (Demodectic Mange Wash; Smith Kline Beecham Animal Health) has also been found to be effective but produced transient sedation in some animals.

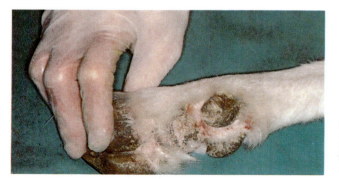

Fig. 21.3
Chorioptic mange.
Lesions on caudal
aspects of the
fetlock.

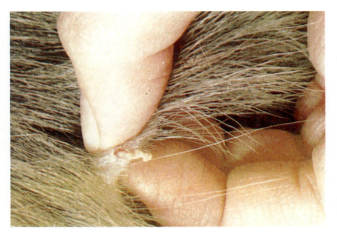

Fig. 21.4
Demodectic mange.
Skin nodule.

Psoroptic mange

Caused by the mite *Psoroptes cuniculi*, psoroptic mange is not notifiable in goats as it is in sheep. The mite normally inhabits the inner surface of the ear where it may be symptomless, but may be associated with head shaking. In other cases scaly lesions may be found on the inner surface of the pinnae, while occasional reports have suggested that in debilitated animals spread may occur to other parts of the skin surface. The condition responds well to application of gamma-benzene hexachloride.

Louse infestation

Pruritus and hair loss are the main features of this problem and may be accompanied by debility and anaemia. The lice and their eggs are chiefly seen on the neck and back. Two species of louse have been recorded in goats: *Damalinia*, a small red burrowing and biting louse, and *Linognathus*, a larger blue sucking louse. Treatment by weekly dusting with gamma-benzene hexachloride is normally effective but must be continued for at least two weeks after the last louse has been seen.

Ticks and fleas

Infestation with these parasites is occasionally seen and is treated with topical insecticides.

Fungal infections

Ringworm

Trichophyton verrucosum is the species of ringworm most frequently seen in goats and lesions (Fig. 21.5) may be confined to the head or extend to other parts of the body. The lesions are initially raised, circular and crusty, later becoming irregular in shape. Close examination reveals broken hairs and evidence of the fungus may be demonstrated microscopically. Treatment with local or oral administration of fungicides is effective.

Bacterial infection

Staphylococcal dermatitis

Staphylococcal pyoderma may be the cause of nodular scabby and usually non-pruritic lesions, especially on the dorsum of

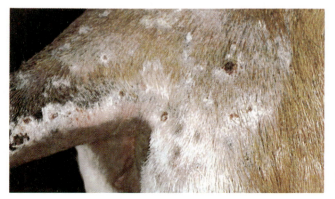

Fig. 21.5
Lesions of ringworm.

Fig. 21.6
Goat with
staphyloccocal skin
infection.

the back (Fig. 21.6). The causal organism, usually *Staphylococcus pyogenes*, can normally be cultured from the dry scaly coat. Sensitivity testing will suggest the antibiotic to be used parenterally for 10 days. Washing with antiseptic solutions such as povidone–iodine at five-day intervals has also been found useful. Histological examination of a biopsy shows characteristic changes (Fig. 21.7).

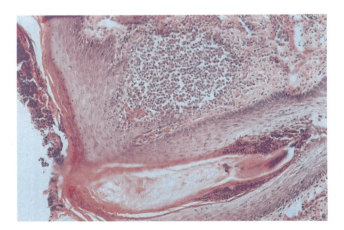

Fig. 21.7
Skin biopsy showing
invasion of skin
layers by bacteria
and polymorphs.

Nocardiosis

Nocardia appears to be an opportunist pathogen which has been found on a number of occasions in chronic subcutaneous abscesses (Fig. 21.8). In some cases a small skin lesion has been found to track deep into muscle and the face or other areas may be involved. Surgical drainage and antibiotic therapy based on sensitivity tests forms the basis of treatment.

Caseous lymphadenitis

This condition, caused by *Corynebacterium pseudotuberculosis* (*C. ovis*), is characterized by subcutaneous abscesses filled with creamy or green coloured pus. The head and neck are common sites but abscesses can occur at other sites associated with superficial lymph nodes. Several animals in the herd may be affected and recurrence is common when abscesses are drained. The condition, which can rarely be contracted by attendants, is subject in the UK to control by MAFF. Suspected cases should be discussed with the local Divisional Veterinary Officer.

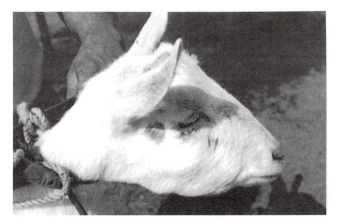

Fig. 21.8
Subcutaneous abscesses on face of goat caused by nocardia.

Virus diseases

Orf

This disease is characterized by scabby lesions normally confined to the lips (Fig. 21.9) and is said to affect older animals more readily than the young, although mortality in kids has been recorded. Lesions may also be seen on the muzzle, nose, buccal mucosa and occasionally the udder. The causal organism – a pox virus – can be demonstrated in fresh scabs by electron microscopy. In mild cases treatment is unnecessary but application of an oxytetracycline–gentian violet aerosol will limit secondary bacterial infection and hasten healing. The dangers of human infection must not be forgotten.

Papillomatosis

Caused by a virus of the papavovirus group, outbreaks of warts, especially on the head and neck, are occasionally seen. When present on the lips there may be some resemblance to orf. True papillomata are circumscribed and of the same consistency throughout and firmly attached to the skin. The lesions of orf by comparison are easily picked off revealing underlying areas of inflammation and granulation.

Fig. 21.9
Goat with orf.

Scrapie

The incidence of this nervous disease has increased in goats in recent years. Although the clinical signs in this species are chiefly neurological, pruritis and self-inflicted skin lesions are occasionally seen.

Auto-immune skin disease

Two cases of pemphigus foleaceous have recently been reported in goats. In the case seen by the author the disease was characterized by crusty pruritic lesions on the skin around the tail, on the scrotum and ventral abdomen. Diagnosis was established by the typical histology of a skin biopsy (Fig. 21.10) and by the demonstration of fluorescent intercellular antibody in the epidermis. Some seasonal remission may be seen and corticosteroid therapy gives some temporary relief.

OTHER SKIN DISEASES

Toxic epidermal necrolysis

A single suspected case of this condition has been seen. Characterized by mucocutaneous ulceration around all the

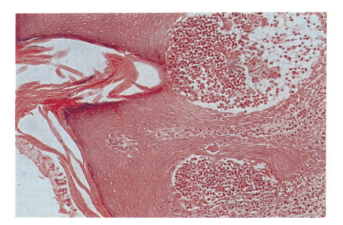

Fig. 21.10
Bullous lesion in the skin of goat suffering from pemphigus foleaceous.

natural orifices (Fig. 21.11) the condition was accompanied by pyrexia and severe depression. The symptoms are most distressing for the patient. The underlying cause is uncertain but may include drug sensitivity. Treatment includes removing this underlying cause, supportive therapy and administration of glucocorticoids. Analgesia is essential and in severe cases, euthanasia.

Sticky kid syndrome

This condition, which has been reported in purebred Golden Guernsey goats, may be associated with a recessive, sex-linked gene. Affected kids are born with a sticky, matted coat which fails to dry out normally after birth (Fig. 21.12). The kid may be rejected by its mother but may be raised with care artificially and although some spontaneous improvement may occur the coat remains harsh and sticky in later life. The condition is associated with excessive production of secretion from the sebaceous glands.

Skin disease in dwarf goats

A serious problem among certain families of dwarf goat, the condition is characterized by non-pruritic crusty lesions

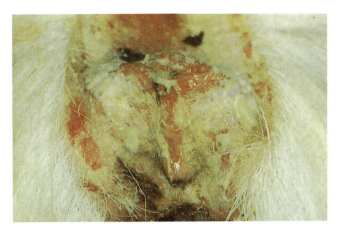

Fig. 21.11
Vulval region of goat suffering from suspected toxic epidermal necrolysis.

Fig. 21.12
Golden Guernsey
suffering from sticky
kid syndrome.

around the eyes, muzzle and ears on the head (Fig. 21.13). Lesions are also seen on the skin of the axilla, groin and perineum. The condition shows some similarities histologically to human psoriasis and a congenital aetiology is suspected. Secondary bacterial infection may occur. Young adults may be particularly badly affected and the condition may regress or occasionally worsen spontaneously in warm weather. In some cases a temporary response to steroid therapy has been reported. The zinc and selenium status of affected animals should be monitored.

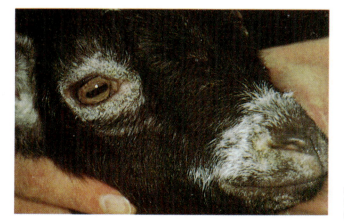

Fig. 21.13
Skin lesions in dwarf
goat.

Cutaneous neoplasia

Although a relatively uncommon problem in goats a number of cases of melanoma have been described, especially in warmer climates. A series of cases of cutaneous haemangioma with concurrent squamous cell carcinoma has been reported in related animals. Lesions were confined to the udder and eventually caused great difficulty at milking time.

Physical and chemical trauma

The inquisitive nature of the goat renders the skin liable to exposure to physical and chemical insult. Treatment consists of removing the causal agent and protecting the skin while healing occurs.

ACKNOWLEDGEMENTS

The author would like to thank Mr Andrew Jefferies for pathological assistance and Dr Sheelagh Lloyd for help and advice. Dr Jill Murphy, Miss Patricia Harris, Mr Murray Corke and Mr Alastair Mews kindly loaned photographs of some of their cases.

Index